WAVELENGTH
TABLES
OF
SENSITIVE LINES

By

L. H. AHRENS, D.Sc., F.R.I.C.

Assistant Professor of Geology at the
Massachusetts Institute of Technology
Formerly Senior Analytical Chemist
of the Government Metallurgical
Laboratory, Johannesburg

1954

ADDISON–WESLEY PUBLISHING COMPANY, Inc.

CAMBRIDGE 42, MASS.

WAVELENGTH TABLES

The most sensitive lines of the elements in the arc and possible interfering lines within ± 0.4 — 0.5 A of each sensitive line. Prepared particularly for the analysis of minerals, rocks, soils, meteorites, and related materials.

————————

The following elements are included and are arranged alphabetically: aluminum, antimony, arsenic, barium, beryllium, bismuth, boron, cadmium, calcium, cerium, cesium, chromium, cobalt, copper, dysprosium, erbium, europium, fluorine, gadolinium, gallium, germanium, gold, hafnium, holmium, indium, iridium, iron, lanthanum, lead, lithium, lutetium, magnesium, manganese, molybdenum, neodymium, nickel, niobium, osmium, palladium, phosphorus, platinum, potassium, praseodymium, rhenium, rhodium, rubidium, ruthenium, samarium, scandium, silicon, silver, sodium, strontium, tantalum, tellurium, terbium, thallium, thorium, thulium, tin, titanium, uranium, vanadium, wolfram, ytterbium, yttrium, zinc, and zirconium.

In accordance with the recommendation of the XVth Conference of the International Chemistry Union, element 74 has been referred to as wolfram and element 41 as niobium.

In the main body of these wavelength tables, the symbol Cb will be found in place of Nb. This part of the wavelength tables had been prepared prior to the announcement of the recommendation of the XVth Conference of the International Chemistry Union.

TABLE OF CONTENTS

Preface

General comments on line sensitivity 1

Line interference 4

Use of symbols 4

Excitation potentials 5

Detection-limit concentrations in the arc 5

Wavelength tables (spectrographic analysis) with notes on
   interference 9

Sensitive rare earth lines according to Smith and Wiggins . 78

Visual sensitivities (spectroscopic analysis) 81

Periodic table of the elements 82

Revisionary data on M.I.T. tables 83

Bibliography 86

PREFACE

In qualitative spectrochemical analysis, two to four of the most sensitive lines of an element usually suffice to establish with certainty whether it is present or absent.* In these tables, such sensi-

*The term *absent* is, of course, a misnomer, and unfortunately is loosely used in qualitative analysis. Almost every element is present at some concentration in any one specimen, and whether the element is actually detectable or not depends on the sensitivity of the method of analysis. A more accurate statement of qualitative analysis would probably be "the establishment of whether an element is detectable, and hence is present above some detection limit concentration, or whether it is undetectable, and hence *if* present (it is difficult to draw the line here – a few atoms could be regarded as *present*) must be below the detection limit concentration." The use of *not detected* is preferable to *absent* or that other unfortunate term, *nil,* which is sometimes used.

It is not necessarily implied that each analyst must know the detection limit for each particular element. If this is known, however, it greatly enhances the value of his statement of analysis; instead of *not detected,* he could state, for example, $<0.001\%$. Table 1 gives information on the detection limits of each element in the d.c. arc.

tive lines are given, together with possible interfering lines (within 0.4–0.5 A of the sensitive line) and are arranged for easy scanning. The tolerance of 0.4–0.5 A should suffice for almost all grating spectrographs, and for prism instruments in the violet and ultra-violet, normally used for the analysis of minerals, rocks, soils, meteorites and allied materials. The wavelengths and approximate relative intensities of all lines are from the M.I.T. Wavelength Tables (Harrison, 1939) unless stated otherwise.

For most elements, the lines given here as the most sensitive are believed to be correct, but for a few, notably Re, Hf, U, Th, and a few rare earths, there is still some doubt. This is due either to a lack of consensus among analysts, inability to make theoretical predictions of the most sensitive lines, or merely a lack of complete information. For each element, a few additional lines are given, which may be employed if for one reason or another the recommended lines cannot be used.

Smith and Wiggins (1949) have made a careful study of the relative sensitivities of rare earth lines. Their observations are given in full on page 78. There the observations of two sets of observers, Smith and Wiggins (S and W), and Meggers and Scribner(M and S) who also participated in the investigation are given. 1, 2, 3, ...

refer to the order of sensitivity found by each pair of observers. When information on the most sensitive rare earth lines is required these observations should be consulted as well as the main wavelength tables.

As the arc is sometimes used for visual (spectroscopic) analysis, sensitive lines have been given for this method. These lines are those recommended by H. W. Jaffe of the U. S. Bureau of Mines, who has kindly placed them at the author's disposal.

Much of the information given in these tables has appeared in the author's book (Ahrens, 1950). However, in these tables some newer information has been included and moreover the preparation of a separate publication has been in the interests of practicability.

For the analysis of such complex substances as minerals, rocks, soils, meteorites, and allied materials, the detailed M.I.T. Wavelength Tables (Harrison, 1939) are a necessity. Some of the more important revised information on the M.I.T. tables that has been brought to the notice of the author has been included here.

ACKNOWLEDGEMENTS

The author is greatly indebted to Mr. E. R. French and Misses S. Bateman and M. M. Kearns for their aid in preparing and checking these tables. Grateful acknowledgment is made to Dean G. R. Harrison for permission to use the M.I.T. tables for the preparation of these tables and for kindly placing at the author's disposal some information which has been used here for the preparation of revisionary data on the M.I.T. tables.

GENERAL COMMENTS ON LINE SENSITIVITY

In attempting to ascertain which line of an element is the most sensitive, and the correct order of relative sensitivities of several of its sensitive lines, many factors come into consideration: for example, variation in sensitivity of the photographic emulsion with change of wavelength; temperature of the arc column; matrix composition; absorption* of radiation in the far ultraviolet by either photographic emulsion, air, or if prism optics are used, quartz; variable reflectivity of a grating; variable background on a spectrogram; and type of spectrograph. Degree of ionization is another factor and is discussed separately (see below).

Theory has been a great aid, particularly as it is not encumbered by the practical considerations given above, and for the most part those lines which have been predicted as the most sensitive (Meggers, 1941 a and b) are indeed so. Where several sensitive lines are components of the same multiplet, theory will frequently show the relative order of sensitivity.

Some of the most sensitive lines of the elements fall in the far ultraviolet and because of absorption are not usable, unless particular precautions have been taken (use of gelatin-free plate and a small vacuum spectrograph — grating or fluorite prism). P 1774, As 1890, and Sb 2068 are examples; Zn 2138 is a borderline example. At the other wavelength extreme are those sensitive lines, Cs 8521 and K 7699, for example, which are located in the far red region. These lines may usually be reached without difficulty by commercially available panchromatic emulsions and are regarded as normally usable lines. With the exception, therefore, of a few lines in the far ultraviolet, the most sensitive lines of all elements excited in the arc are normally usable.

Ionization in the arc is a complicating factor when attempting to assess the relative sensitivities of lines in the spectrum of an element. Theory can usually inform us which line or lines in the spectrum emitted by the *atom* of an element is the most sensitive, and which line or lines emitted by the *ion* of the element is the most sensitive. At the elevated temperatures (3000-8000° A) at which arcs

---

*Absorption by the gelatin of the photographic emulsion increases sharply at about 2200 A. In oxygen, absorption begins at about 1950 A, and in nitrogen at about 1450 A. Quartz shows significant absorption below about 1950 A; at 1850 A absorption by quartz is almost complete.

1

operate, some ionization takes place and its degree will depend on the temperature of the arc and the ionization potential of the particular element, as indicated by Saha's equation (see, for example, Ahrens, 1950, Chap. 3). Those elements which have only one excitable electron outside closed shells, the alkali metals for example, do not emit an ion spectrum in the arc because of the tightness with which the "closed shell" electrons are held. Elements with more than one electron outside closed shells are capable of emitting an ion spectrum as well as an atom spectrum. The degree of ionization then controls which (the most sensitive atom line or the most sensitive ion line) is the most sensitive line for the element, under the particular conditions of working. An example will illustrate this point. Calcium, like all alkaline earths and particularly strontium and barium, emits very sensitive ion lines as well as sensitive atom lines in the arc. The most sensitive atom line is Ca 4226 and the most sensitive ion line is Ca 3933. When these lines are emitted from a relatively cool arc (3000-4000° A) obtained by arcing potash *feldspar,* for example, the ratio *I* Ca 4226/*I* Ca 3933, is approximately 3, and the atom line has greater persistence. In a hot source (7000-8000° A), as is produced by a carbon arc with no material added to the electrodes, the intensity ratio is about 0.5 or less, and the ion line has greater persistence.

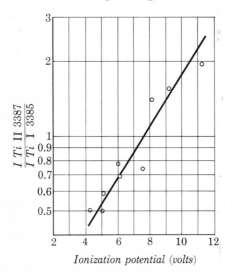

Fig. 1. The ratio of a titanium atom-ion line pair is seen to vary sharply with the ionization potential (and hence temperature) of the arc gas. This relationship is general for all atom-ion line pairs.

A good illustration of how differently atom and ion lines respond to a variation in temperature of the arc is shown in Fig. 1, a plot of the ratio of a pair of titanium lines, (I Ti II 3387/I Ti I 3385) vs. ionization potential of the dominant element in the arc. [For the relationship between temperature and the effective ionization potential of the arc gas, see Ahrens (1950, Chap. 3).] Over a range of ionization potentials of 4.3 volts for potassium (lowest temperature) to 11.2 volts for carbon (highest temperature), the intensity ratio varies by a factor of about 4. For ionization potentials up to about 7.5 volts, the atom line Ti 3385 is more intense, whereas above about 8 volts, the ion line 3387 is more intense. Figure 1 is based on the data given by Preuss (1938). Although he used cathode-layer excitation, such behavior of the atom-ion line intensity ratio to a change of temperature applies irrespective of whether anode or cathode excitation has been employed.

With regard to the respective sensitivities of atom and ion lines in the d.c. arc, elements may be grouped into four categories.

(1) Atom (arc) lines most sensitive lines, with ion line emission absent or weak. This category comprises a major proportion of the 70-odd elements excitable in the arc.

EXAMPLES: Li, Na, K, Rb, Cs, Ag, Au, Cu, Cd, Zn, Ga, In, Tl, B, Te, the platinum group, Sn, W, and Si.

(2) Atom lines most sensitive lines in normally used arcs but ion lines reasonably persistent.

EXAMPLES: Mn, Ni, V, Mg, Cr, Mo, Be, Nb, and Fe.

Although the atom lines are usually the most sensitive, consideration must be given to arc temperature because in relatively hot arcs ion lines may sometimes exhibit greater persistence.

(3) Either the most sensitive atom line or the most sensitive ion line may be regarded as the most persistent.

EXAMPLES: Ca, Sr, and Ba.

The above comments on change of intensity of Ca 4226 and Ca 3933 to change in temperature apply equally well to the sensitive atom and ion lines of Sr and Ba.

(4) Ion lines may usually be regarded as the most persistent lines.

EXAMPLES: Ti, Sc, Zr, Y, and a large proportion of the rare earth elements (see individual members in tables).

Although ion lines of the elements of this group are usually the most sensitive, atom lines sometimes show greater persistence in relatively cool arcs.

LINE INTERFERENCE

In his recent book, Dingle (1950, p. 122) makes the statement that some 50% of publications on spectrochemical analysis during the last thirty years contain errors, mainly those of reporting the presence of elements which are at concentration levels far below detection limits. His figure is probably a little high, but nevertheless it is true that a far too high proportion of analyses of minerals, rocks and soils, and related materials show evidence of such errors. With the hope that these errors of commission, particularly by beginners, may be reduced and that such information may be of general use, some comments based on observed examples of line interference are given in these tables. Such comments should in no sense be regarded as complete. One glance at the main body of the M.I.T. tables will show that, almost without exception, each sensitive line of an element *could* have interference provided an appropriate compound were present at a high enough concentration. Consequently it would be well nigh impossible to attempt discussions of all possible examples of line interference, particularly when the vastness of the mineral kingdom is taken into consideration. The comments given here are for the most part restricted to actual observations of line interference in the relatively common minerals types, rock groups, and soils.

USE OF SYMBOLS

To indicate the relative order of sensitivities of lines, letters of the alphabet have been introduced, where (a) denotes a line of greater sensitivity than one labelled (b), and so on. For some elements, one line listed in the (a) category may be slightly, but definitely, more sensitive than another; for example, two components of a multiplet. Use is then made of (aa), (a), ... (bb), (b), where the symbol (aa) indicates the line as slightly, but definitely, more sensitive than (a). Thus, the four sensitive rubidium lines and their corresponding symbols are:

$$
\begin{array}{ll}
7947 & \text{(a)} \\
\underline{7800} & \text{(aa)} \\
4215 & \text{(b)} \\
4202 & \text{(bb)}
\end{array}
$$

Rb 7800 is the most sensitive line of rubidium and is about twice as intense as 7947. Both these lines are considerably more intense than the blue lines, for which Rb 4202 is twice as intense as Rb 4215. Each pair of lines is a multiplet pair.

An underscore thus, _____, means that the line has been predicated from theory as the most sensitive line of the atom, whereas an underscore thus, – – –, refers to the theoretically most sensitive ion line. (See Meggers, 1941, a and b.) An inspection of the wavelength tables shows that for nearly every element, an underscored line is symbolized as (aa) or (a). There is therefore close accordance between theory and practical observation. For explanation of the symbols w, W, l, wh, h, r, R, and s, consult M.I.T. Wavelength Tables (Harrison, 1939).

EXCITATION POTENTIALS

For each line excitation potentials (in volts) are given for low and high levels. The excitation potential of the high level is the excitation potential of the line as usually understood. For ion lines, the low and high level excitation potentials refer to their heights above the ground state of the *ion*. First ionization potentials are also given in volts.

DETECTION-LIMIT CONCENTRATIONS IN THE D.C. ARC

Table 1 gives the approximate detection-limit concentrations for most elements which are excited in the d.c. arc.

A few of the detection limits given in Table 1 do not accord with the comments made by the author (Ahrens, 1950) on the sensitivities of some elements. Cesium is an example. Where such discrepancies exist, the values given in Table 1 should be used.

The given detection limit for each element is based on the use of its most sensitive line as listed in these tables. With the exceptions of zinc (see footnote to Table 1), the wavelength range covered by these lines is 2200-9000 A. The far ultraviolet is thus excluded. Those elements which have their most sensitive lines in the far ultraviolet may have detection limits lower than given in Table 1 provided the necessary precautions are taken to eliminate the absorption of radiation below about 2200 A. These procedures are regarded as special techniques and therefore detection limits attainable by their use are not given here. Some analysts who have given

TABLE 1

APPROXIMATE DETECTION-LIMIT CONCENTRATIONS OF
ELEMENTS USING D.C. ARC EXCITATION

Element	%	p.p.m.	Element	%	p.p.m.
Ag	0.00005	0.5	Na	0.00005	0.5
Al	0.0002	2	Nb	0.003	30
As	0.01	100	Nd	0.001	10
Au	0.001	10	Ni	0.0005	5
B	0.001	10	Os	0.005	50
Ba	0.0005	5	P	0.01?	100?
Be	0.001	10	Pb	0.0005	5
Bi	0.002	20	Pd	0.001	10
Ca	0.0002	2	Pr	0.001	10
Cd	0.001	10	Pt	0.005	50
Ce	0.05	500	Ra		
Co	0.001	10	Rb	0.0001	1
Cr	0.0001	1	Re	0.01	100
Cs	0.0002	3	Rh	0.001	10
Cu	0.00005	0.5	Ru	0.001	10
Dy	0.001	10	Sb	0.002	20
Er	0.001	10	Sc	0.0002	2
Eu	0.001	10	Si	0.002	20
F	0.01	100	Sm	0.05?	500?
Fe	0.0005	5	Sn	0.001	10
Ga	0.0003	3	Sr	0.0005	5
Gd	0.02?	200?	Ta	0.01?	10
Ge	0.0005	5	Tb	0.001	10
Hf	0.01?	100?	Te	0.02	200
Hg	0.01	100	Th	0.01	100
Ho	0.001?	10?	Ti	0.001	10
In	0.0001	1	Tl	0.0001	1
Ir	0.005	50	Tm	0.001?	10?
K	0.0002	2	U	0.01	100
La	0.001	10	V	0.0005	5
Li	0.0001	1	W	0.002	20
Lu	0.001?	10?	Y	0.001	10
Mg	0.0002	2	Yb	0.001	10
Mn	0.001	10	Zn	0.0003*	3
Mo	0.0005	5	Zr	0.001	10

* Refers to Zn 2138; 0.01% if more commonly used lines (Zn 3345, for example) are used.

tables of detection limits give values such as 0.1 or 0.05% for potassium and rubidium. Evidently these values refer to the so-called blue lines (see wavelength tables) because far lower detection limits are attainable provided the red lines and panchromatic plates are used.

There will, of course, never be real consensus among spectrochemists on the detection limits of elements: far too many variables of instrumentation and of conditions of operation are involved. Table 1 should, however, usually indicate the attainable magnitudes within a factor of three.

Should the analyst desire to lower the detection limit of a particular element as far as possible, considerably lower concentrations than those given in Table 1 can usually be reached. This may be done by adjusting the operating conditions to suit the particular element and its line as follows: correct choice of plate; use of a large dispersion; superposition of several exposures on a plate of high contrast; correct timing of the exposure so as to record only the period of peak intensity of emission during the whole period of volatilization of the sample; choice of optimum electrode cavity size and shape; use of a compound for enhancing the intensity of a given line (for example, the addition of an alkali metal salt for enhancing low temperature lines); use of the most effective amperage; and so on. One example will illustrate this. Thallium is a sensitive element, and has been given a detection limit of .0001% in Table 1. However, by adjusting operating conditions as indicated above, F. C. Canney, working in the Cabot Spectographic Laboratory, has been able to reach concentrations as low as about .00002-.00001%, that is, about $\frac{1}{5}$ to $\frac{1}{10}$ of that given above.

Ionization Potential, 5.96

	Most Sensitive Lines		Excitation Potential Low	High
3961.527	I	(aa)	0.0	3.13
3944.032	I	(a)	0.0	3.13
3092.713	I	(bb)	0.0	4.0
3082.155	I	(b)	0.0	4.0

Eu	3961.99	10w	Er	3944.014	2	W	3092.285	7
Mo	3961.988	3	Eu	3944.01	8h	Hf II	3092.245	20
U	3961.984	6	Ce II	3943.888	40	Zr	3092.240	3
Tb	3961.970	3	U	3943.820	35			
Sm	3961.808	25	Pr	3943.753	10			
W	3961.760	5	Th	3943.694	10	Co	3082.618	150R
Ce	3961.661	6	Cb	3943.666	20	Ti I	3082.615	6
U	3961.660	1	V I	3943.664	50	U	3082.587	6
Zr	3961.587	500	Tb	3943.66	8	Tm	3082.57	10
Yb	3961.544	30	Gd	3943.631	20	Sc II	3082.56	2
			Sm	3943.621	8	V	3082.523	3
Al I	3961.527	3000	Cr I	3943.614	18	Dy	3082.515	15
Ru	3961.518	6				Ta	3082.447	15h
U	3961.515	8				Re I	3082.432	100w
Mo	3961.503	5	Ce	3093.243	6	Tb	3082.36	3
Ce	3961.386	2	Tm	3093.12	30	Ce	3082.304	20
Ag	3961.3	15	V II	3093.108	100R	Rb I	3082.27	10
Pr	3961.284	10	Dy	3093.108	15	Sm	3082.261	1
Er	3961.210	6	Th	3093.055	12	Mo	3082.220	4
Fe I	3961.145	25	U	3093.012	20	Th	3082.176	10
Eu	3961.14	50w	Ta	3092.994	18	Yt II	3082.167	4
U	3961.064	6	Mg I	3092.991	125			
Re I	3961.033	30	Nd	3092.915	8	Al I	3082.155	800
			Cb	3092.886	1h			
Eu	3944.592	5w	Al	3092.842	50R	V	3082.111	80R
Er	3944.423	12	Ce	3092.818	4	Er	3082.08	12
Nd	3944.421	20	Fe	3092.778	50	Mn	3082.052	50
Ir I	3944.375	20	Na II	3092.729	50	Th	3082.031	12
Re	3944.349	15	Ce	3092.724	4	U	3082.020	8
Th	3944.254	3	V	3092.720	100r	V I	3082.012	15
Tb	3944.20	6	U	3092.720	5	Gd	3082.000	100
Ru I	3944.190	10				Ce	3081.984	5
Pr	3944.137	9	Al I	3092.713	1000	Mo	3081.950	25
U	3944.130	8				W	3081.864	10
Ni I	3944.126	5wh	Yt	3092.712	8	Ta	3081.850	50
Ce II	3944.093	8	Mo	3092.70	20	Fe	3081.84	2
Ir	3944.058	2	Sc II	3092.519	3	Cb	3081.769	1
			Ta	3092.444	50	U	3081.666	6
Al I	3944.032	2000	Sc	3092.42	3			
Rh	3944.019	5	Ir	3092.401	5			
Re	3944.016	15	Fe	3092.399	4			
			Cd II	3092.393	10			

Antimony (Sb)

Ionization Potential, 8.64

Most Sensitive Lines			Excitation Potential	
			Low	High
2877.915	I	(b)	1.0	5.3
2598.062	I	(b)	1.05	5.8
2528.535	I	(b)	1.2	6.1

Os	2878.400	40	Zr II	2877.551	4	O	2597.572	10
Mo	2878.382	20	Pt II	2877.520	40	Ru	2597.518	10
Tm	2878.36	10	Ti II	2877.436	30			
W	2878.30	1						
U	2878.240	5				Co I	2528.967	50R
Tm	2878.21	3	Ru	2598.581	20	W	2528.912	3
Ta	2878.20	4	Fe	2598.47	1	Fe	2528.879	2
Cb	2878.165	2	W	2598.421	10	Ru	2528.878	60
W	2878.079	4	Fe II	2598.369	700	Mo	2528.866	1
V	2878.022	2	Ir I	2598.284	8	V	2528.836	25
Ce	2878.018	2	Ce	2598.250	5	U	2528.77	5
Cr II	2877.978	30	Ta	2598.21	2s	Ru	2528.715	30
Sb I	2877.915	250W	Mn	2598.174	12	Mn	2528.702	12
			W	2598.107	6	Co II	2528.615	4
Ca	2877.91	1h	Rh	2598.072	4	Ta	2528.59	4
Eu	2877.890	2						
Dy	2877.885	2	Sb I	2598.062	200	Sb I	2528.535	300R
Cb	2877.852	2						
Ru I	2877.840	3	Cb	2598.041	2	Si I	2528.516	400
U	2877.830	2	Fe II	2598.028	4	Dy	2528.49	4
Eu	2877.76	5	Ir I	2598.000	2	V	2528.468	50
Cu II	2877.689	5	Re	2597.964	20	Ce	2528.287	15
V	2877.688	15	Ir	2597.862	3	Cr I	2528.244	30
Ta	2877.686	15	Fe	2597.828	6	Fe	2528.174	6
Ir I	2877.678	20	W	2597.726	10	U	2528.099	10
U	2877.569	6	Rh I	2597.683	2	Ni I	2528.050	20

Sb 2068.38 is theoretically the most sensitive line of antimony, but its wavelength is just below the usual working range of wavelengths.

Because of its high sensitivity, Si 2528.516 will commonly interfere with Sb 2528.535, even in sulfide ores which have only a trace of siliceous gangue.

Other sensitive *antimony* lines: 3267.502, 3232.499 and 2311.469.

Ionization Potential, 10

| | | Excitation Potential | |
Most Sensitive Lines		Low	High
2860.452	I (c)	2.3	6.6
2780.197	I (c)	2.3	6.7
2349.84	I (b)	1.4	6.6

Zr I	2860.851	15	Cr I	2780.703	600R	Co I	2350.280	12
U	2860.801	15	Fe	2780.700	30	Os	2350.23	30
Rh I	2860.762	30	Fe	2780.54	10	Zr	2350.20	2
Dy	2860.70	2	Eu	2780.526	20	Ir	2350.054	15
W	2860.679	6	Bi I	2780.521	200w	Os	2350.04	12
Pt II	2860.678	30	Ir I	2780.409	3	Cb	2350.028	2
Rh I	2860.675	30	W II	2780.283	10	Ti	2349.94	3
Ir I	2860.665	12	Cb	2780.245	30	Cd	2349.857	2
Ce	2860.643	2	La II	2780.234	20	Sb	2349.853	8
Hf	2860.557	20	Ta	2780.208	4	U	2349.85	2h
Ce	2860.555	3				Cu	2349.85	5
Tm	2860.55	10	As I	2780.197	75R			
U	2860.466	35	U	2780.040	8	As I	2349.84	250R
As I	2860.452	50r	Mo	2780.036	60	W	2349.82	6
			Ce	2780.005	15	Os	2349.81	40
Yb	2860.40	1	Mn	2779.998	25	V	2349.806	3w
Ru	2860.374	3	Mg	2779.834	40	Mo	2349.78	10w
Hf II	2860.312	15	Ce	2779.825	2	Yt	2349.70	8
Ti I	2860.277	7	Sn	2779.817	80	Rh	2349.68	3
Er	2860.257	4	La	2779.778	1	Ir	2349.662	5
Fe	2860.21	2				Dy	2349.63	3
Dy	2860.172	2				Re	2349.61	12
W	2860.163	5				Zr	2349.59	10
Tm	2860.13	15				Re	2349.40	12
Os	2860.063	25						
Ru I	2860.016	60						
V I	2859.971	50						

Theoretically, As 1890.5 is the most sensitive atom line of arsenic, but its wavelength is below the normally usable range.

Other sensitive *arsenic* lines: 2898.71, 2456.53 and 2288.12.

Barium (Ba)

Ionization Potential, 5.19

Most Sensitive Lines			Excitation Potential	
			Low	High
5535.551	I	(a)?	0.0	2.23
4934.086	II	(a)	0.0	2.50
4554.042	II	(aa)	0.0	2.73

Eu	5536.13	30		Fe	4934.023	40
U	5535.796	6		Ni I	4934.000	3
La II	5535.671	50		Th	4933.852	8
Ba I	5535.551	1000R		Dy	4933.845	2
				W	4933.822	12
Sm	5535.504	3		Re	4933.740	15w
Nd	5535.476	3		Mo	4933.732	12
Fe	5535.411	50		U	4933.657	8
V I	5535.382	2		Zr I	4933.643	4
Tb	5535.38	15		Fe	4933.627	2
Nd	5535.271	2		Ta	4933.527	5s
Ce	5535.240	15				
Pr	5535.176	10		Ru I	4554.509	1000R
Gd	5535.16	8		Pr	4554.498	2
Rh	5535.04	80		Yt I	4554.459	3
				Sm II	4554.443	60
La II	4935.618	8		Ce	4554.333	2
Yb	4935.502	200		Dy	4554.234	2
Er	4935.498	35		Ba II	4554.042	1000R
Sm	4935.458	20				
Pr	4935.380	2		Ce	4554.035	35s
bh Mg	4935.3	4		Mo	4554.028	1
Co I	4935.222	2		Zr II	4553.967	4
Pr	4935.136	2		Cr	4553.949	20
La II	4934.825	150		U	4553.858	4
Ru	4934.607	4		Th	4553.85	3
Hf II	4935.45	40		Cb	4553.836	5
Mn	4934.15	25		Mo	4553.798	20
Th	4934.088	4		Hf	4553.776	10
Ba II	4934.086	400h		Ce	4553.755	2
				bh Pb	4553.7	6
Er	4934.074	18		Ta	4553.694	200ℓ
Pr	4934.071	3		W	4553.662	6
Co	4934.065	25		Yb	4553.561	20

Ba 4554.042 is freer from interference than Ba 5535.551 and Ba 4934.086, both of which are prone to interference from iron in iron-rich minerals, rocks, and soils; Fe 5535.411 with Ba 5535.551, and Fe 4934.023 with Ba 4934.086. Other sensitive *barium* lines: 5777.665, 5519.115 and 4130.664.

Ionization Potential, 9.28

Most Sensitive Lines			Excitation Potential	
			Low	High
3321.343	I	(c)	2.7	6.43
3131.072	II	(b)	0.0	3.94
3130.416	II	(bb)	0.0	3.94
2348.610	I	(a)	0.1	5.40

Eu	3321.857	30	U	3131.325	8	Ir	3130.285	4
U	3321.707	5	Tm	3131.26	400	Fe	3130.278	5
Ti II	3321.700	15	Ta	3131.216	5h	V II	3130.267	50
V I	3321.685	12	Cr	3131.211	20	La II	3130.25	3
Ti I	3321.588	15	Os	3131.115	125	Sm	3130.235	5
W	3321.565	8	Zr I	3131.110	7	Ce	3130.197	15
V	3321.538	3	Be II	3131.072	200	Ti I	3130.175	2
Re	3321.462	10				Dy	3130.159	4
Th	3321.453	10	Er	3131.07	3	W	3130.155	5
Nd	3321.395	8	Th	3131.070	12	Zr I	3130.063	3
Be I	3321.343	1000r	Ho	3130.99	6	Ag	3130.009	25h
			Ce	3130.919	5			
Ce	3321.275	3	Ce	3130.872	30			
Ru	3321.254	12	Gd	3130.814	3	Bi I	2349.10	10
Ni I	3321.242	4	Ti II	3130.800	25	U	2348.91	2
Mo	3321.196	1	Rh I	3130.790	60	La II	2348.86	2h
Cr	3321.19	20	Cb	3130.786	100	Mo	2348.84	3
Sm II	3321.184	50	Eu	3130.74	100W	Mn	2384.83	3
Tb	3321.15	30	U	3130.732	10	Cu II	2348.82	15d
W	3321.133	6	Ir	3130.578	3	Re	2348.80	9
Be I	3321.086	100	Ta	3130.578	100W	Cb	2348.748	3w
Be I	3321.013	50	Ba I	3130.570	2	Ni I	2348.74	10
Pd I	3320.987	15	Fe II	3130.567	4	Os	2348.61	3
Ce II	3320.940	10	Cr	3130.565	1	Be I	2348.610	2000R
U	3320.92	1	Ce	3130.516	5			
Mo	3320.902	3	W	3130.456	10	Zr	2348.586	15
						W	2348.56	2h
			Be II	3130.416	200	Pt II	2348.548	3
Ce	3131.505	2d	Ti I	3130.376	2	Ru	2348.327	50
Os	3131.481	20	U	3130.373	3h	Fe II	2348.303	5
Fe	3131.455	2h	Ce	3130.334	30	Ir	2348.301	20
Tb	3131.35	8	Ta	3130.29	15ℓ	W	2348.151	8

Bismuth (Bi)

Ionization Potential, 8

Most Sensitive Lines			Excitation Potential	
			Low	High
4722.552	I	(c)	1.4	4.02
3067.716	I	(a)	0.0	4.02
2897.975	I	(b)	1.3	5.60

Mo	4723.063	10		Re I	3067.390	60
Sm	4722.947	3h		Rh	3067.305	80
Ta	4722.877	200		Fe I	3067.244	300
V I	4722.865	20				
Bi I	4722.831	10				
U	4722.726	40		Ta	2898.425	30
Er	4722.703	12		Mo	2898.386	2
Pr	4722.670	5		U	2898.366	4
Sm	4722.632	3h		Fe	2898.355	100
Ti I	4722.616	80		Ir I	2898.350	10
				Ce	2898.336	6
Bi I	4722.552	1000		Be I	2898.27	20
Sr I	4722.278	30		Th	2898.267	4
Bi I	4722.190	10		Hf I	2898.259	50
Zn I	4722.159	400w		Zr	2898.256	4
Th	4722.109	2		W	2898.253	8
				Be I	2898.19	15
				Fe	2898.06	2
Fe	3068.176	150		U	2898.013	6
Zr II	3068.024	2		Mn	2897.990	15
Mo	3067.997	30				
Fe	3067.944	15		Bi I	2897.975	500WR
Ir	3067.939	2h		V	2897.896	1
Ce	3067.895	6		Pt I	2897.873	400
W	3067.866	3		Fe	2897.85	2
Eu	3067.784	7		Cb	2897.812	15
U	3067.758	8		Mn	2897.797	15
Sn	3067.755	10		La II	2897.76	2
Th	3067.734	12		Ru	2897.715	6
				Cr	2897.704	3
Bi I	3067.716	3000hR		Yt II	2897.676	3
Sm	3067.672	15		Ir	2897.653	3
Eu	3067.672	8		Fe	2897.64	4
Mo	3067.642	10		U	2897.636	3h
W II	3067.568	3		Rh	2897.633	2
Ce	3067.443	4		Mo	2897.628	20
Hf	3067.414	30		Re	2897.592	10d
W II	3067.41	2		Er	2897.518	12

Fe 3067.244 is an intense iron line and is evident in many bismuth containing minerals. Line interference does not occur unless the spectrograph is small, but as Fe 3067 is a strong line, halation interference sometimes masks Bi 3067 excessively.

Boron (B)

Ionization Potential, 8.28

Most Sensitive Lines			Excitation Potential	
			Low	High
2497.733	I	(aa)	0.0	4.9
2496.778	I	(a)	0.0	4.9

V	2498.044	7	Fe	2496.991	20
Ge I	2497.963	8	Hf II	2496.986	30
Mo	2497.863	20	Cb	2496.973	1
Fe II	2497.820	15	Ta	2496.957	2
B I	2497.733	500	B I	2496.778	300
Sn	2497.720	8	Sn	2496.768	10
Fe II	2497.717	1	Re	2496.70	20
Ru	2497.678	50	W II	2496.638	10
V I	2497.655	4h	Ta	2496.635	20
Th	2497.59	3	Fe	2496.533	40
Mo	2497.580	30h	Zr II	2496.480	2
Co	2497.501	1	Gd	2496.40	2
W II	2497.484	10	Cr I	2496.309	125r
W	2497.292	5	Ir I	2496.271	10
V I	2497.099	2	Ta	2496.237	2h

Cadmium (Cd)

Ionization Potential, 8.96

	Most Sensitive Lines		Excitation Potential	
			Low	High
3466.201	I	(c)	3.7	7.3
3261.057	I	(b)	0.0	3.78
2288.018	I	(a)	0.0	5.4

Ce	3466.646	2		Pt I	3261.072	3
Tb	3466.57	8		Cd I	3261.057	300
Th	3466.536	5				
U	3466.503	3		Ir I	3260.998	2h
Fe I	3466.500	30		Ce II	3260.975	25
Eu	3466.416	30		Ca	3260.93	1h
U	3466.30	8		Th	3260.922	8
Pr	3466.237	2		Zr	3260.916	2h
Cd I	3466.201	1000		Eu	3260.883	5
				Tb	3260.83	15
U	3466.139	4		Co I	3260.819	70
Dy	3466.12	2		B II	3260.74	4
Ce	3466.077	5		Dy	3260.69	10
Ce	3466.029	3		Nd	3260.655	10
Re I	3465.983	20		Os	3260.568	15
Tb	3465.98	30				
Th	3465.929	5				
Hf II	3465.92	5		Rh	2288.57	25
Cb	3465.865	30		Mn	2288.42	6
Fe I	3465.863	500		Ni I	2288.39	12
Mo	3465.86	5		Pt II	2288.192	15
Co I	3465.800	2000R		Sb	2288.139	5
Th	3465.766	10		As I	2288.12	250R
				V	2288.095	3h
Yb	3261.509	5		Cd I	2288.018	1500R
Fe	3261.333	25				
Ce II	3261.242	8		Ir	2287.878	20
Dy	3261.22	5		Ta	2287.84	5
W	3261.165	10		Co	2287.809	12d
Ru	3261.129	30		Ru	2287.68	60
Ce	3261.116	2		W	2287.67	10
Th	3261.11	5		Ni II	2287.65	2
V	3261.081	15		Fe I	2287.630	5
Zr I	3261.078	2h		Ru	2287.525	3

Other sensitive *cadmium* lines 6438.47, 3610.51 and 3466.201.

Ionization Potential, 6.09

	Most Sensitive Lines			Excitation Potential	
				Low	High
	4226.728	I	(a)	0.0	2.92
	3968.468	II	(b)	0.0	3.11
	3933.666	II	(bb)	0.0	3.14

U	4227.330	6	Th	3969.003	10	Nd	3934.093	20
Gd	4227.145	50	Nd	3968.876	20	Ce	3934.076	6
Mo	4227.085	3	Eu	3968.870	3wh	V I	3934.013	100
Nd	4226.992	6	Mo	3968.748	8	U	3933.985	6
W	4226.915	15	Tb	3968.73	2	Co I	3933.914	60
Cr	4226.758	125	Zr	3968.723	3	Tb	3933.905	4
Ir	4226.735	30	W	3968.590	6	Ir	3933.901	20
Ce	4226.734	50	Ir	3968.475	25	Ce	3933.731	60
			Cb	3968.471	3	Ru	3933.680	5
Ca I	4226.728	500R	Ce	3968.469	35	Eu	3933.677	10
Yt	4226.726	5						
Mo	4226.726	15	Ca II	3968.468	500R	Ca II	3933.666	600R
Ru I	4226.656	15	Lu	3968.464	50	Hf II	3933.664	20
Ir	4226.628	5	Ru	3968.461	12	Ir	3933.664	20
V I	4226.624	8	Yt	3968.43	10	U	3933.662	2
U	4226.60	1	Dy	3968.395	300	Co	3933.654	80
Ge I	4226.570	200	U	3968.374	1	Ag	3933.62	80
Mo	4226.549	10	Fe	3968.370	2	Fe I	3933.605	200
Os	4226.527	12	Gd	3968.35	20	Sm II	3933.592	200
Tb	4226.44	50	Zr I	3968.257	100	Tb	3933.469	6
Fe I	4226.430	80	Ag	3968.22	100	Cb	3933.394	3
W	4226.343	10	W	3968.171	8	Sc I	3933.381	60
Ce	4226.335	2	Rh I	3968.164	2	Pr	3933.300	9
Mo	4226.291	20	Ta	3968.16	4h	Zr I	3933.178	9
Cb	4226.247	4	Pr	3968.158	25			
			Tb	3968.146	2			
			V II	3968.094	25			
			Hf	3968.01	5			
			U	3968.007	6h			
			Fe I	3967.969	60			

Fe 3933.605 is intense and appears in the spectra of many minerals, rocks, and soils.

Other sensitive *calcium* lines: 4434.960 and 3158.869.

Cerium (Ce)*

Ionization Potential, 6.9

Most Sensitive Lines			Excitation Potential	
			Low	High
4296.680	II	(c)?	0.0	2.87
4222.599	II	(c)?	0.0	2.92
4186.599	II	(a)	0.4	3.33
4133.800	II	(b)	0.0	3.02
4012.388	II	(c)	0.6	3.64

Gd	4297.179	100
U	4297.112	18
Cr I	4297.050	100
Ir	4297.030	3
Ni I	4296.984	2
Gd	4296.90	4
Sr	4296.82	3
Ce	4296.786	5
Rh I	4296.770	40
Er	4296.752	10d
Sm	4296.750	100
Zr II	4296.742	3
Ru	4296.689	7
Ce II	4296.680	40
Cr	4296.631	15
Mo	4296.624	15
Fe II	4296.585	2
Pr	4296.55	15
Hf	4296.41	10
Ce	4296.371	10
Nd	4296.363	12
Tb	4296.35	20
Dy	4296.34	2
Gd	4296.291	40
Cr	4296.275	15
Os	4296.218	12
Pr	4296.18	10
Sm	4223.056	3
Gd	4222.98	10
Pr	4222.98	125
Mo	4222.961	15
U	4222.94	1
Tb	4222.91	6w
Ce	4222.884	3
Na I	4222.8	3
U	4222.739	6
Cr I	4222.732	100
Tb	4222.71	9
Tm	4222.67	10
Ce II	4222.599	80

Mo	4222.411	20
U	4222.375	18
Eu	4222.31	5
Ho	4222.26	3
Dy	4222.221	10
Fe I	4222.221	200
P	4222.15	300
Fe I	4187.044	250
U	4186.977	10
Ce	4186.860	2
Ho	4186.84	3
Dy	4186.810	100w
U	4186.790	6
Zr I	4186.777	3
Er	4186.71	8
Zr II	4186.688	3
Tb	4186.60	2
Ce II	4186.599	80
U	4186.477	6
Eu	4186.42	6
Pr	4186.395	12
Cr	4186.359	50
Nd	4186.311	25
Tm	4186.31	5
Mo	4186.281	15
Ir	4186.280	2
Tb	4186.24	10
Ti I	4186.123	100
Fe I	4134.340	2
Zr I	4134.314	8
Tb	4134.31	4
Gd I	4134.167	25
Dy	4134.14	12
Th	4134.117	10
Dy	4133.863	15
Fe I	4133.862	50
Ce II	4133.800	35

Sm	4133.797	2
V I	4133.777	9
Ce	4133.715	3
Zr I	4133.695	5
Pr	4133.618	10
Tb	4133.55	2
Zr I	4133.524	4
U	4133.492	15
W	4133.482	6d
Cb	4133.418	2
Re I	4133.417	200
Dy	4133.370	10
Nd	4133.361	15
La	4133.334	15
U	4013.029	8
Pr	4012.91	8
Tb	4012.87	6
Dy	4012.82	5
Eu	4012.816	20
Ti I	4012.806	12
Mo	4012.80	3
U	4012.708	2h
Nd	4012.704	15
Er	4012.58	4
Dy	4012.523	4
Mo	4012.51	3
Th	4012.497	15
Cr	4012.469	70
Tb	4012.45	5
Ti II	4012.391	35
Ce I,II	4012.388	60
Mo	4012.270	3
Re	4012.260	25
Er	4012.253	12
Zr I	4012.252	20
Nd	4012.250	80
U	4012.161	6
Co I	4012.160	2
Ce	4012.139	4
Ta	4012.111	5h
Mo	4011.966	25
Hf	4011.944	3
Mn	4011.905	12

*See list of sensitive rare earth lines at end of tables.

Other sensitive *cerium* lines: 4137.646, 4040.762 and 3942.151.

Ionization Potential, 3.87

			Excitation Potential	
Most Sensitive Lines			Low	High
8943.50	I	(a)	0.0	1.38
8521.10	I	(aa)	0.0	1.45
4593.177	I	(b)	0.0	2.69
4555.355	I	(bb)	0.0	2.71

Fe I	8945.204	20	Fe II	4555.895	12
Re	8944.56	2	Th	4555.815	3
Cs I	8943.50	2000R	Eu	4555.71	12W
			Er	4555.693	3
Fe I	8943.00	3	Ce	4555.620	2
Zr I	8941.74	3	Cb	4555.561	3h
			Zr I	4555.52	30
			Ti I	4555.489	125
Ba I	8521.96	2	Ce	4555.425	5
Mn I	8521.57	10h	Eu	4555.38	4
Cs I	8521.10	5000R	Cs I	4555.355	2000R
Ti I	8518.32	100	W	4555.327	7
			Yt I	4555.298	2
			Cr	4555.296	15
Mo	4593.643	8	Tm	4555.26	25
Pr	4593.571	8d	Dy	4555.24	4
Sm II	4593.531	50	Nd	4555.140	15
Sm	4593.407	2	Zr I	4555.130	15
Yb	4593.37	4	U	4555.095	20
Th	4593.290	3	Cr	4555.092	15
Ru I	4593.213	7	Ti I	4555.083	12
Cs I	4593.177	1000R	Th	4555.071	3
			Gd	4554.99	6
Ce	4593.103	3	Nd	4554.967	5
Tb	4593.06	3	Cr	4554.830	25
Ru	4593.025	6			
Sc I	4592.939	2			
U	4592.933	3			
Er	4592.93	3			
Fe I	4592.655	200			

Ti 8518.32 is emitted from many silicate minerals, rocks, and soils, but does not interfere with Cs 8521.10 in grating spectrographs, or in large glass-prism spectrographs.

Emission from Ti 4555.083 is evident in the spectra of most rocks, soils, and some minerals, and could therefore interfere with Cs 4555.355 in prism spectrographs. However, cesium is a rare element and Cs 4555 is detectably emitted only in some potassium minerals (*lepidolite, muscovite, biotite, phlogopite*, and sometimes *potash feldspar*) and here, with the exception of *biotite*, Ti 4555 is usually absent.

The comments which apply above to Cs 4555 and Ti 4555 apply in much the same way to Cs 4593.177 and Fe 4592.655.

Chromium (Cr)

Ionization Potential, 6.74

	Most Sensitive Lines			Excitation Potential	
				Low	High
	4289.721	I	(a)	0.0	2.88
	4274.803	I	(aa)	0.0	2.89
	4254.346	I	(aaa)	0.0	2.90

Mo	4290.184	30h	W	4274.938	10
Ho	4290.17	2	Os	4274.905	9
W	4290.144	8	Cb	4274.892	5
Mn	4290.112	8	**Cr I**	**4274.803**	**4000R**
Gd	4290.067	6			
Ce	4289.938	50	Zr I	4274.769	9
Ti I	4289.919	15	Cb	4274.689	5
Gd	4289.901	40	Ti I	4274.584	100
Pr	4289.89	15	W	4274.550	20
U	4289.882	12	Ti I	4274.400	5
Tb	4289.73	30	Tb	4274.36	2h
Cr I	**4289.721**	**3000R**			
U	4289.556	4	Ce	4254.905	8
Ce II	4289.454	25	Yb	4254.77	4
Cb	4289.444	10	N I	4254.75	15
Pr	4289.42	12	Ce	4254.701	20
Mo	4289.415	20	Cb	4254.694	10
Sm	4289.365	15	Th	4254.458	8
Ca I	4289.364	35	Ho	4254.43	100
Nd	4289.363	15	Mo	4254.429	10
Dy	4289.35	2	V II	4254.425	3
W	4289.291	1	Pr	4254.420	35
Ti I	4289.073	125	Cb	4254.392	10
			Ce	4254.370	8
Pr	4275.32	5	**Cr I**	**4254.346**	**5000R**
Tb	4275.21	15	Er	4254.32	7
Pr	4275.17	12	W	4254.288	4
W	4275.149	6	Bi I	4254.152	10
Cu I	4275.131	80	W	4254.060	8
Nd	4275.083	20	Gd	4254.03	3
Co I	4275.069	3	Ce	4254.004	3
U	4275.02	2	Tb	4254.00	5
Dy	4275.00	5	Fe	4253.93	2
Pr	4274.959	3	Th	4253.875	6

Ti 4274.400 is sometimes emitted by rocks and soils and may interfere with Cr 4274.803 if prism optics are used.

Other sensitive *chromium* lines: 5208.436, 3578.69 and 2835.633.

Ionization Potential, 7.86

	Most Sensitive Lines			Excitation Potential	
				Low	High
	3453.505	I	(a)	0.4	4.00
	3405.120	I	(b)	0.4	4.05

Th	3453.922	4	Th	3405.561	3
Eu	3453.88	2w	Ce	3405.444	6
Pt	3453.86	1	Cb	3405.411	80
Pr	3453.784	6	Bi	3405.326	40
U	3453.780	4	W	3405.277	7
Ce	3453.760	3	Ru	3405.277	3
Cr I	3453.743	30	Cr	3405.22	12
Tm	3453.66	150	Mo	3405.204	8
Ti I	3453.654	3	V I	3405.160	30
Ce	3453.639	2	Co I	3405.120	2000R
U	3453.570	5			
Sm	3453.547	15	Ti I	3405.094	20
Ti I	3453.531	5h	Ag	3405.03	3
Co I	3453.505	3000R	Dy	3404.99	4
			V I	3404.960	8
Re I	3453.502	40	U	3404.933	3
Eu	3453.47	3	Ce	3404.910	18
Tb	3453.46	15	Mo	3404.864	6
Cr I	3453.328	35	Zr II	3404.832	40
Re	3453.285	20	W	3404.803	8
Ce	3453.241	8	Sm	3404.767	2
Sm	3453.226	4	Nd	3404.763	4
La II	3453.168	50	Fe I	3404.754	2
Ho	3453.13	30	Re I	3404.724	100
Dy	3453.12	5wh	Tb	3404.71	3
Er	3453.10	12	Th	3404.654	4
Os	3453.054	20s			

Whereas Co 3405.120 may sometimes have interference from Ti 3405.094 in some rocks, soils, and minerals, more sensitive Co 3453.505 is invariably free from interference.

Other sensitive *cobalt* lines: 3529.813, 3465.800 and 2286.156.

Copper (Cu)

Ionization Potential, 7.68

	Most Sensitive Lines		Excitation Potential	
			Low	High
	3273.962	I (a)	0.0	3.77
	3247.540	I (aa)	0.0	3.80

Fe	3274.453	80	Ce	3247.898	3
Th	3274.399	6	Tb	3247.79	8
Eu	3274.29	3	U	3247.709	4
Tb	3274.24	70	Ir I	3247.667	3
Na II	3274.220	15	Mo	3247.621	30
Ce	3274.112	8	Ce	3247.552	15
Ce	3274.064	10	Ag	3247.55	15
Ti I	3274.047	7	Sb	3247.547	2h
Ce	3273.964	5	Mn	3247.542	125
Cu I	**3273.962**	**3000R**	**Cu I**	**3247.540**	**5000R**
Mo	3273.961	20	Eu	3247.530	50W
Ca	3273.958	2	Er	3247.52	18d
Co	3273.931	10	Cb	3247.474	50w
Ce	3273.926	5	Sm	3247.366	4
Cb	3273.886	20r	Eu	3247.30	4
Th	3273.884	10	Fe I	3247.278	20
Hf II	3273.655	20	Cr I	3247.274	20
Ru	3273.621	2	Ce	3247.250	3
Sc I	3273.619	35	Fe	3247.213	10
U	3273.596	5	U	3247.209	2
Ce	3273.516	4	Tb	3247.18	15
			Co I	3247.179	80
			Sm	3247.17	1
			Ce	3247.118	3
			La I	3247.04	8

Mn 3247.542 is emitted from several basic rocks and mafic minerals and in such materials quite often interferes with Cu 3247.540.

Ionization Potential, 6.8

Most Sensitive Lines			Excitation Potential
4211.719		(b)?	
4045.983	I	(b)?	
4000.454	II	(b)?	
3531.712		(a)	

Tb	4212.23	3w	Ce II	4045.973	5	Gd	4000.16	10h
Zr I	4212.158	3	Tb	4045.97	25	V I	4000.078	8
Ru I	4212.063	125	Ho	4045.95	10			
Cb	4212.040	4	Er	4045.89	2	Ta	3532.208	15
Gd	4212.019	150	Gd	4045.862	30	Mn	3532.121	50h
Ce	4211.906	1	Ag	4045.82	10	Ir	3532.06	2d
Zr II	4211.875	18	Fe I	4045.815	400	Ru	3532.055	5
Cu II	4211.861	1h	Ru	4045.762	25	U	3532.051	1
Pr	4211.858	50d	Zr II	4045.612	10	Sm	3532.008	5
Os	4211.855	150	W	4045.601	12	Mn	3531.998	50h
Mn	4211.748	30	Cb	4045.590	1	Th	3531.935	4d
Ho	4211.73	5	Mo	4045.543	3	Mn	3531.848	40R
Ti I	4211.728	30	Ho	4045.43	200	Eu	3531.832	12
Tb	4211.72	25	Eu	4000.807	3	Ir I	3531.798	2
			Ce	4000.799	4	Ru	3531.794	8
Dy	4211.719	200	U	4000.732	6	Ho	3531.74	10
			Eu	4000.698	3	Er	3531.714	40
Er	4211.716	30	W	4000.694	12			
U	4211.68	10	Ce	4000.675	5	Dy	3531.712	100
U	4211.620	18	Cr	4000.63	5	Nd	3531.712	6
Ce	4211.582	3	Ho	4000.62	4	Yt	3531.707	7
Th	4211.519	8	Cb	4000.605	2	Tb	3531.70	15
Cr	4211.349	100	Nd	4000.562	8d	U	3531.641	15
Zr I	4211.335	12	Mo	4000.497	8	Pr	3531.623	4
U	4211.310	10	Nd	4000.493	10d	Ce	3531.593	18
Nd	4211.286	30	Pr	4000.478	8	Ta	3531.584	35
Dy	4211.248	4	Tb	4000.46	15	Th	3531.451	4
Pr	4211.24	5				Fe I	3531.446	3
			Dy	4000.454	400	Nd	3531.39	4
Sc I	4046.486	10	Fe	4000.452	35	Ru	3531.390	60
U	4046.402	3	Er	4000.452	35	Mo	3531.303	3
Ce I,II	4046.340	30	Ho	4000.45	5	Er	3531.264	12
Cb	4046.27	3	Mo	4000.386	6	Yb	3531.25	2
V	4046.264	1	Th	4000.287	8	Hf	3531.227	5
Sm II	4046.154	12	Fe I	4000.266	8			
Zr I	4046.082	3	Pr	4000.190	50			
Dy I	4045.983	150						

*See list of sensitive rare earth lines at end of tables.

Other sensitive *dysprosium* lines: 4186.810, 3944.692 and 3407.80.

Erbium (Er)*

Ionization Potential,

Most Sensitive Lines   Excitation Potential

4007.967	(b)?
3906.316	(b)?
3692.652	(b)
3372.750	(a)

Ce	4008.446	6	Hg I	3906.410	25	Yt I	3692.529	7
Nd	4008.416	5				Ru	3692.370	6
Gd I	4008.331	15	Er	3906.316	25	Rh I	3692.357	500hd
Sm	4008.330	8	Co I	3906.294	150	Pr	3692.293	4
Cb	4008.280	5	Pt I	3906.291	2			
Ru I	4008.269	20	Ho	3906.26	3	Co I	3373.230	60
Th	4008.216	10	Zr	3906.151	3	Eu	3373.228	3
Er	4008.185	8	Ce	3906.104	2	Os	3373.204	6
V II	4008.169	2	Nd	3906.096	15	Mo	3373.126	5
Sm II	4008.091	10	Pr	3906.093	6	Nd	3373.095	4
Ti I	4008.062	50	Fe II	3906.037	2w	Os	3373.038	15
Mo	4008.054	4	Ba I	3906.010	4	Pd I	3373.001	800r
Ir I	4008.052	12	Ru	3905.991	6	Pt	3372.996	10
Mn	4008.020	15	W	3905.970	8	Mo	3372.920	5
Eu	4007.98	6	Dy	3905.95	6	Fe	3372.861	2
			Ce	3905.920	3	Ti II	3372.800	80
Er	4007.967	35	U	3905.896	8	Pr	3372.797	10
Ho	4007.96	4	Nd	3905.886	40	Th	3372.794	3d
Co I	4007.943	3				Pt	3372.791	2
U	4007.934	8	Ta	3693.047	35r	Ho	3372.79	12
Pr	4007.78	8	Fe	3693.032	15	Yt	3372.77	15
Dy	4007.77	12	Tb	3692.95	30			
Tb	4007.75	3	U	3692.91	5	Er	3372.750	35
U	4007.689	2	Sm	3692.899	10	Tb	3372.72	50
Eu	4007.687	5d	Mn	3692.812	50	Th	3372.696	1d
La	4007.662	3	Nd	3692.768	12	Ca	3372.68	1
Zr I	4007.601	25	Sm	3692.763	20	Ce	3372.648	3
Ce	4007.588	15	U	3692.750	10	U	3372.600	4
Ru	4007.535	20	W	3692.725	7	Cb	3372.562	10h
			Ir I	3692.694	15	Ce	3372.539	8
Hf	3906.89	3	Eu	3692.66	5w	Rh I	3372.526	10
Sm II	3906.805	6				Os	3372.524	3
Th	3906.796	8	Er	3692.652	20	Pr	3372.510	20
Fe	3906.751	10	Fe	3692.652	5	Ag II	3372.505	1
V I	3906.748	50	Ho	3692.65	10	Ce	3372.391	3
Tb	3906.53	4	Mo	3692.645	3	Tb	3372.36	15
Fe I	3906.482	300	Zr II	3692.635	2	Fe	3372.351	1
Mo	3906.480	5	Th	3692.571	10	Rh I	3372.254	300
Ce	3906.452	8	Ce	3692.552	2			

*See list of sensitive rare earth lines at end of tables.

Another sensitive *erbium* line: 3499.104.

Ionization Potential, 5.64

Excitation Potential

Most Sensitive Lines				Low	High
4594.02	I			0.0	2.69
4205.046	II	(b)		0.0	2.93
3907.11	II	(c)?		0.2	3.36
3819.66	II	(a)		0.0	3.23

Pr	4594.572	3	Eu	4204.909	5	V I	3820.297	25
Nd	4594.447	10	Gd	4204.839	25	W	3820.109	8
Cr	4594.403	10	Sm II	4204.813	8	Ir	3820.088	4
Tb	4594.31	2	Mo	4204.809	25	Ce	3819.999	4
U	4594.294	6	Ce	4204.739	15	Cr I	3819.981	12
Ce	4594.129	4	Yt II	4204.696	15	Nd	3819.965	15
Mn	4594.108	12	Mo	4204.609	15	V I	3819.963	60
V I	4594.108	30wh	Pr	4204.58	5	Hf	3819.925	12
			Os	4204.560	12	Co I	3819.910	20
Eu	4594.02	500R				Pt	3819.88	3
Er	4594.01	2	Ag	3907.59	3	Mo	3819.873	6
Yt	4594.00	3	U	3907.558	6	Mo	3819.778	6
Tb	4593.947	4	Sc I	3907.476	125	Ru I	3819.767	12
Nd	4593.936	2h	Fe	3907.470	15	Ta	3819.713	5
Ce	4593.932	30	Ce	3907.445	6	Nd	3819.703	2
Pr	4593.926	30	Th	3907.342	8	Sm	3819.678	10
bh La	4593.9	5	Pr	3907.296	8			
Cr	4593.831	12	Ce	3907.289	35	Eu II	3819.66	500wd
Ce	4593.716	2	W	3907.202	6	Cr I	3819.564	60
Mo	4593.643	8	V	3907.17	2h	Ce	3819.534	2
Pr	4593.571	8d	Gd	3907.125	100W	Fe	3819.50	2
			Sm	3907.124	10	Hf	3819.376	15
Fe	4205.546	50				Th	3819.28	2
Sm	4205.361	8	Eu II	3907.110	1000RW	Er	3819.271	12d
Cb	4205.311	15	U	3907.018	5	Ce	3819.204	3
Nd	4205.255	5	Mo	3906.976	5	Cb	3819.147	12
Tb	4205.23	2	Ce	3906.924	8			
Os	4205.222	9	Mo	3906.916	5			
Sc I	4205.194	10	Cb	3906.906	5			
Ce	4205.161	6	Hf	3906.89	3			
bh Ca	4205.1	6	Sm II	3906.805	6			
V II	4205.086	5	Th	3906.796	8			
Eu II	4205.046	200R	Fe	3906.751	10			
			V I	3906.748	50			
Dy	4205.03	7	Tb	3906.53	4			
			Fe I	3906.482	300			

*See list of sensitive rare earth lines at end of tables.

Eu 4594.02 is theoretically the most sensitive atom line of europium, but it does not appear to be particularly sensitive in commonly used arcs. The same applies to the theoretically most sensitive atom lines of Y, La, Sm, and Gd, but not Yb.

Other sensitive *europium* lines: 4129.737 and 3930.503.

Fluorine (F)

Most Sensitive Bands			Excitation Potential	
			Low	High
CaF:	6064 (sub-head)	(a)	0.0	2.0
"	5291.0 (head)	(b)	0.0	2.3
"	5292.9	(b)	0.0	2.3
"	5296.8	(b)	0.0	2.3
"	5298.6	(b)	0.0	2.3

and other components of this sequence.

SrF:	5772.0	(b)	0.0	2.1
"	5779.5	(b)	0.0	2.1

and other members of this sequence.

According to the observations of R. Seraphim, working in the Cabot Spectrographic Laboratory, M.I.T., CaF 6064 is considerably more intense ($\times$ 5.5) than the band with head at λ 5291, but is not in common use because of strong interference from CaO emission at 6000-6200A. This frequently swamps CaF 6064 emission excessively in most rocks, minerals, and soils unless excitation is in an inert atmosphere for example, helium. For details of the structure of the CaO band, see Pearse and Gaydon (1950), Plate 1.

Gadolinium (Gd)*

Ionization Potential 6.16

Most Sensitive Lines			Excitation Potential	
			Low	High
4262.095	II	(c)?	0.7	3.62
4251.736	II	(c)?	0.4	3.28
3646.196	II	(c)	0.25	3.62
3422.466	II	(a)	0.25	3.84
3362.244	II	(b)	0.1	3.62

Tb	4262.59	2	Dy	3646.60	5	U	3422.352	18r
Ce	4262.367	2	W II	3646.525	10ℓ	Ni I	3422.332	10
Cr	4262.356	30	U	3646.491	2	Mo	3422.309	10
La I	4262.334	15	Tb	3646.46	8	Rh I	3422.291	12
Pr	4262.314	10	Pr	3646.299	50	Os	3422.275	20
W	4262.269	7	U	3646.217	10	Pr	3422.26	5
Nd	4262.239	15	Ti I	3646.200	70	Ce	3422.215	2
Eu	4262.177	2	Gd II	3646.196	200w	Sm II	3422.189	3
V I	4262.161	20				Fe	3422.14	2
U	4262.155	6	Cr	3646.161	18	Dy	3422.07	3
Cr	4262,133	40	Ru	3646.114	2	Sm	3422.063	5
Gd II	4262.095	150	Sm	3646.013	2	Ce	3422.000	5
			bh Sr	3646.0	4			
Cb	4262.053	20	Pd I	3646.968	15	Cr I	3362.711	40
Ir	4261.888	10	Er	3645.938	15	Zr II	3362.684	6
Nd	4261.837	20	Cb	3645.929	1	Th	3362.672	3
Tb	4261.83	8	Sm II	3645.898	4	Ti II	3362.653	2
bh Ca	4261.8	2	Dy	3645.86	6	Tm	3362.61	250
Pr	4261.796	15	Fe	3645.825	80	Os	3362.559	2
Eu	4261.794	4	Sm	3645.789	5d	Th	3362.533	3
Cb	4261.714	5	Nd	3645.776	8	Ta	3362.530	10r
Cr	4261.615	35	Ce	3645.711	2	Yb	3362.43	15
			Pr	3645.660	30	Mo	3362.366	25
Cr I	4252.243	35	Tb	3423.05	15	Ru	3362.335	50
Ni I	4252.107	2	Co I	3422.896	18	Ca I	3362.28	2
Pr	4252.07	4	Ni I	3422.878	10	Fe	3362.279	6
Er	4251.938	18	Dy	3422.878	15	Nd	3362.262	12
Mo	4251.873	60	Er	3422.87	3d	Gd II	3362.244	150
Ce	4251.858	10	Cb	3422.849	1			
Sm II	4251.788	200	Cb	3422.786	3r	Cr I	3362.213	80
Ti I	4251.761	10	Co	3422.784	7	Th	3362.196	3
Gd II	4251.736	300	Sm	3422.760	9	Rh I	3362.184	100
			Cr II	3422.739	35	Dy	3362.17	3
Dy	4251.73	7	Gd	3422.713	8	Ca I	3362.131	15
Tb	4251.72	12	Ce	3422.708	30	Ti I	3362.100	6
Ti I	4251.606	20	Ti II	3422.661	4	U	3362.050	2
Ce	4251.602	8	Fe I	3422.660	100	La I	3362.040	10
Pr	4251.490	40w	Th	3422.657	3	Ru I	3362.003	60
Yb	4251.489	15	Er	3422.62	4	Yt II	3362.000	12
Mo	4251.389	5	Dy	3422.57	10d	W	3361.971	4
Ce	4251.364	5	Ce	3422.507	18	Fe	3361.952	6
Tb	4251.33	10	Fe	3422.493	40	Sc II	3361.935	25
U	4251.326	10	Sm	3422.476	2	Ca I	3361.918	125
Sm	4251.303	2	Er	3422.471	6	Ce II	3361.853	8
Yt I	4251.205	25	Gd II	3422.466	80	W	3361.852	6
						Ti I	3361.835	12
Eu	3646.660	10W	Tb	3422.44	3	Re	3361.833	4
Ce	3646.652	10	W	3422.426	10	Nd	3361.773	8
Re	3646.628	10	Ce	3422.420	8	Cr II	3361.770	10
						Ce	3361.762	25

*See list of sensitive rare earth lines at end of tables.

According to theory, Gd 4225.85 is the most sensitive atom line of gadolinium. It does not appear to have very high persistence, however; cf. Y, La, Eu, and Sm.

Other sensitive *gadolinium* lines: 3768.405 and 3350.482.

Gallium (Ga)

Ionization Potential, 5.97

Most Sensitive Lines			Excitation Potential	
			Low	High
4172.056	I	(aa)	0.1	3.06
4032.982	I	(a)	0.0	3.06
2943.637	I	(b)	0.1	4.3

Ir I	4172.559	150	Cr I	4033.263	30	Ru	2943.921	50
La I	4172.316	8	Pr	4033.24	3	Ni I	2943.914	50r
Pr	4172.273	75	Cb	4033.203	5	Mn	2943.908	2
Ho	4172.23	2	Sr I	4033.191	6	U	2943.895	10
Yb	4172.23	2	Mn I	4033.073	400r	Ir	2943.87	4d
U	4172.18	3	Cr	4033.072	15	V I	2943.827	7h
Ce II	4172.161	18	Ta	4033.069	100	Sm	2943.786	8
Fe	4172.127	80	In	4033.066	4	Ta	2943.769	10
Ga I	4172.056	2000R	Tb	4033.04	125	Ir	2943.725	3h
Dy	4171.992	15	Ga I	4032.982	1000R	Ce	2943.673	8
Ce	4171.964	2	Sm	4032.977	20	Ga I	2943.637	100*
Dy	4171.925	4	Pr	4032.974	15	V	2943.636	2
Ti II	4171.903	15	V I	4032.856	2	Ir	2943.628	3h
Pr	4171.824	75	Dy	4032.847	8	Fe	2943.57	12
Tb	4171.80	8	Ce	4032.748	2	La II	2943.551	2
Ce	4171.769	2	Tb	4032.705	3	Nd	2943.500	3
Gd	4171.71	25	Ti I	4032.632	35	Sm	2943.492	8
Er	4171.708	15	Fe I	4032.630	80	Co I	2943.484	30
Fe	4171.700	8	Tb	4032.626	4	Ru I	2943.481	30
Cr	4171.675	70	Ce	4032.554	3	U	2943.405	6
U	4171.591	30	Th	4032.54	10	Mo	2943.380	1
			Cb	4032.524	30	Re I	2943.380	15
						Tm	2943.36	6
Gd	4033.491	10	Ga	2944.175	10	W	2943.326	7
U	4033.427	12	Er	2944.071	12	Ir	2943.260	4
Ce	4033.378	2h	Ce	2943.987	6	Ce	2943.215	6
Re I	4033.307	40	W	2943.959	5	V I	2943.196	30

*The M.I.T. tables assign an intensity value of "10" to Ga 2943, which is a sensitive line much used by spectrochemists. Because this very low intensity value may be misleading, an intensity of "100" is given above.

Excessive interference by CN 4216 with Ga 4172 is almost inevitable unless CN emission is effectively reduced. As gallium is a volatile element, such interference may be reduced to a negligible proportion by exposing only the early period of arcing, during which the alkali metals volatize (Ahrens, 1950, Chap. 10). Most rocks and many minerals carry a sufficient concentration of alkali metals for this purpose.

Ga 4032.982 invariably has excessive interference from Mn 4033.073 in almost every rock and soil, and in most minerals.

The M.I.T. tables assign an intensity value of only "10" to this line. Ga 2943 is sensitive and much used and has been given an intensity of "200" here.

Another sensitive *gallium* line: 2874.244.

Ionization Potential, 8.09

	Most Sensitive Lines			Excitation Potential	
				Low	High
	3269.494	I	(b)	0.9	4.65
	3039.064	I	(c)	0.9	4.94
	2651.178	I	(a)	0.1	4.8

Fe	3269.959	5	Ca I	3039.21	1h
Sc I	3269.904	30	Cb	3039.187	2
Os	3269.887	8	U	3039.136	5
U	3269.779	10	Sm	3039.128	15
Eu	3269.66	4wh	Ge I	3039.064	1000
Zr I	3269.657	12			
W	3269.628	10ℓ	Ce	3038.993	4
Dy	3269.527	2	Nd	3038.962	4
Ge I	3269.494	300	Ru	3038.784	3
			Ti II	3038.706	2
Th	3269.469	10	V	3038.706	20
U	3269.458	2	Ho	3038.69	4
Eu	3269.414	2	Tb	3038.66	8
Er	3269.411	18	Mn	3038.602	3
Fe	3269.235	20	Th	3038.600	12
U	3269.229	2			
Os	3269.209	200			
Ta	3269.140	70r	Fe I	2651.706	60
Ce	3269.129	10	Ge I	2651.575	30
Dy	3269.12	20	Ru	2651.507	20
Cb	3269.117	2	Ta	2651.483	50
Ca I	3269.101	10	W	2651.441	9d
Re	3269.037	30	Ce	2651.418	2
			Ru I	2651.292	60
			Ge I	2651.178	400*
U	3039.501	10			
Cb	3039.406	3	Hf II	2651.165	15
Sm	3039.358	6	Cb	2651.122	3
In I	3039.356	1000R	W	2651.023	1
Fe	3039.316	20	Ce	2651.006	25
W	3039.311	10	Pt I	2650.857	700
U	3039.263	15	Be I	2650.781	25
Ir I	3039.260	25	Yb	2650.74	2
Ce	3039.253	4	W	2650.711	2

*An intensity value of "40" for Ge 2651 listed in M.I.T. tables seems low, and an approximate value of "400" is given here.

In some sulfide minerals which carry detectable concentrations of germanium, In 3039.356 may be in evidence. In most spectrographs no line interference with Ge 3039.064 will occur, but there may be halation interference.

An intensity value of "40" for Ge 2651 listed in the M.I.T. tables seems low, and an approximate value of "400" is given here.

Other sensitive *germanium* lines: 3269.494 and 2754.59.

Gold (Au)

Ionization Potential, 9.22

Most Sensitive Lines			Excitation Potential	
			Low	High
2675.95	I	(b)	0.0	4.6
2427.95	I	(a)	0.0	5.1

U	2676.410	4	Mn	2428.422	12
Ce	2676.355	2	Fe II	2428.361	3
Ru	2676.353	50	Ir I	2428.360	2
Mn	2676.331	15	Ti I	2428.359	8
Rh	2676.25	1	Co II	2428.293	10
Ru	2676.190	8	Fe II	2428.286	1
Cb	2676.125	2	V I	2428.279	30r
Ce	2676.121	2	Ti I	2428.228	15
Fe	2676.11	15w	Pt I	2428.203	100
Rh I	2676.110	10	Fe	2428.20	9
Ti I	2676.080	6	Ag II	2428.196	1
Co I	2675.982	10w	W	2428.173	5
V I	2675.973	6	Sr I	2428.095	10h
			Pt I	2428.035	100
Au I	2675.95	250R	Th	2427.99	3
Cb	2675.944	10	Ir	2427.963	5
Ta	2675.901	150			
U	2675.880	15	Au I	2427.95	400R
W	2675.869	12	Os	2427.900	8
V I	2675.761	12	W II	2427.813	1
Ce	2675.733	2	V I	2427.745	6
Cr	2675.682	1	Ru	2427.741	2
Th	2675.670	8	Ta	2427.642	150
La II	2675.655	2	U	2427.622	12
Ta	2675.54	2	Ir I	2427.613	25
W	2675.400	10	Cb	2427.539	5
			W II	2427.490	10d

If gold is sought in siliceous material, SiO bands usually interfere strongly with Au 2676 and Au 2428, particularly the latter. SiO emission may be reduced by arcing in an inert atmosphere. In an air atmosphere significant reduction of SiO emission may be attained by exposing only the early period of arcing, because gold is more volatile than silicon.

Ionization Potential, 5.5

Because of a lack of information on the spectrochemical
analysis of traces of Hf, it has not been possible to list
the most sensitive lines of Hf with certainty. Several
sensitive lines have been given by authors, but little has
been said about the most sensitive. Petersen (1927)[1]
examined the lines of Hf between 2500 - 3500 A, and reported the ion line at 2773.357 A as the most sensitive,
and 2866.373 and 2919.594 as the next most sensitive;
other persistent lines reported were 2516.881, and
2887.135, 2898.259, 2904.408, 2904.751, 2940.772, 2964.876
and 3194.193. De Rubies and Agaudo (1935)[2] give in addition to 2516, 2773, 2898, 2904, 2940, the following lines:
2513.028, 2641.406, 2820.224, 2916.481, 3072.877, 3134.718
and 4093.161. Meggers (1928)[3] has also given a list of
sensitive lines, most of which have been listed above.

[1] Peterson, M., Nature, 119, 352-353, 1927.

[2] De Rubies, S. P., Agauda, J. G., Annales, Soc. Espan.
Fis. Quim., 33, 549, 1935.

[3] Meggers, W. F., U. S. Bur. Stds. Jour. Res., 1, 151-187,
1928.

Holmium (Ho)*

Ionization Potential,

Most Sensitive Lines   Excitation Potential

3981.02   (b)
3748.17   (c)?
3456.00   (a)

Eu	3891.48	3w	Cr I	3748.614	40	Ce II	3456.340	10
Ru	3891.410	20	Ir I	3748.564	3	U	3456.297	3
Re	3891.398	15	Cb	3748.554	10	Mo	3456.152	5
Zr I	3891.383	100	Ce	3748.527	2	Os	3456.139	20
Eu	3891.34	4w	Sm	3748.515	5	Sm	3456.114	4
Cb	3891.300	50	Pr	3748.504	5	Ce	3456.031	2
W	3891.249	9	Fe II	3748.490	2h	Dy	3456.01	40w
V I	3891.220	8	Mo	3748.490	15	Nd	3456.004	4
Sm II	3891.179	50	Ca I	3748.374	12	Er	3456.003	25d
V	3891.119	5	Th	3748.304	10			
U	3891.090	10	Fe I	3748.264	500	Ho	3456.00	60
Yt	3891.083	2h	Rh I	3748.217	200	Tb	3455.99	8
Th	3891.060	10				Pr	3455.972	30
			Ho	3748.17	60	Th	3455.949	4
Ho	3891.02	200	Sm	3748.153	5	U	3455.933	3
			Mo	3748.13	1	Zr I	3455.908	12
Ce II	3890.986	12	Ti I	3748.102	10	Sc I	3455.898	3
Tb	3890.95	5	Pr	3748.058	9	Nd	3455.767	2
Nd	3890.940	20	Ce	3748.056	10	Ti I	3455.755	6
Gd	3890.884	15	Ti II	3748.003	2	U	3455.742	5
Yt	3890.858	4	La	3747.99	2	Ru	3455.732	12
Fe	3890.844	60	V I	3747.982	50	Ho	3455.70	6
Ce	3890.761	8	Dy	3747.827	60	Cr	3455.602	50
Cb	3890.749	2	Ti I	3747.782	7	Ce	3455.471	2
W	3890.741	7	Sm	3747.753	3			
Ta	3890.714	2	Tb	3747.64	30			
Mo	3890.706	5						
Er	3890.619	10	Th	3456.441	5			
Ba I	3890.583	3	Co I	3456.437	5			
Nd	3890.580	30	Ti II	3456.390	25			
Ce II	3890.527	4	Mo	3456.387	15w			
Tm	3890.52	40						

*See list of sensitive rare earth lines at end of tables.

Other sensitive *holmium* lines: 4103.84 and 3796.73.

Ionization Potential, 5.76

			Excitation Potential	
			Low	High
Most Sensitive Lines				
4511.323	I	(a)	0.27	3.01
3256.09	I	(b)		3.01

Nd	4511.823	50	Ru I	4511.197	25	Th	3256.273	10
Pr	4511.815	3	Ti	4511.170	40	Ce	3256.251	12
U	4511.746	5h	Zr I	4511.170	5	Dy	3256.25	25
Er	4511.715	4w	U	4511.158	4	Ce	3256.232	6
Ce	4511.635	10	Pr	4511.091	3	W	3256.230	8
Eu	4511.53	3w	Cb	4511.089	5	Mo	3256.210	40
Tb	4511.52	40	Ta	4510.982	200W	Mn	3256.137	75
Ta	4511.503	300	Ce	4510.921	6	In I	3256.09	1500R
Pr	4511.455	5	Er	4510.917	2w			
V I	4511.432	2	Ho	4510.81	2	W	3255.962	9
Pr	4511.349	4				Pt I	3255.916	3
Cd	4511.34	5				Fe II	3255.890	20
In I	4511.323	5000R	La	3256.601	3	Sm	3255.843	6
			V	3256.46	8	Ca	3255.811	1h
Sm	4511.307	40	U	3256.458	2	Re	3255.801	4
Sn	4511.30	200	Pt	3256.433	2	Er	3255.787	10
Nd	4511.290	25	Er	3256.35	10	Ta	3255.69	18h
Pt I	4511.257	2	Ru	3256.331	50	Sc I	3255.678	15
Mn	4511.238	2	Re	3256.289	8	V I	3255.649	25

In 3256.09 is sometimes detectable in micas, notably *lepidolite*. There it must be used with caution because of interference from Mn 3256.137. Indium is more volatile than manganese, and consequently interference may be lessened by recording only the early period of arcing. In 3248 may be used as a check line for interference (Ahrens, 1950, Chap. 9); see same publication for use of In 3256 for quantitative analysis in the presence of interference from Mn 3256. In manganiferous *sphalerite*, Mn 3256 interferes with In 3256.

Other sensitive *indium* lines: 4101.773 and 3039.356.

Iridium (Ir)

Ionization Potential, 9.2

		Excitation Potential	
Most Sensitive Lines		Low	High
3220.78	(b)?	0.35	4.18
3133.321	(b)?		
2543.971	(a)?		

Ni I	3221.273	35	Gd	3133.859	25	Ce	2544.376	2
Yb	3221.22	2	W	3133.716	6	U	2544.358	8
W	3221.212	12d	Ru	3133.697	12	Ce	2544.269	3
Ru	3221.190	4	Th	3133.619	10	Ta	2544.267	2
Ce II	3221.171	50	Nd	3133.603	15	Co I	2544.253	50r
Ti I	3221.151	4	Ta	3133.553	15	Rh	2544.223	8
Cb	3221.125	4	Ce	3133.533	2	Ru	2544.222	60
Tm	3221.08	7	Hf II	3133.50	15	Re	2544.214	25
Ce	3221.061	2	Zr II	3133.475	6	Au I	2544.19	30
Cb	3220.927	10	U	3133.424	8	W	2544.172	8
Ce	3220.871	30	Ce	3133.407	5	U	2544.042	4
Mo	3220.855	8	V II	3133.328	50	Cb	2543.981	4
Rh	3220.78	4	Ce	3133.327	20			
						Ir I	**2543.971**	**200h**
Ir I	**3220.780**	**100**	**Ir I**	**3133.321**	**40**			
						Rh	2543.941	15
Pt	3220.778	2	Eu	3133.24	10	Fe	2543.920	40
Er	3220.730	25	Zr I	3133.231	5	Na I	2543.875	12R
Hf II	3220.606	25	Fe	3133.226	5	Re	2543.831	20
Pb	3220.538	50h	Cd I	3133.167	200	Dy	2543.82	10
Nd	3220.529	2h	Tb	3133.15	8	Na I	2543.817	6R
Cb	3220.488	3h	Ti I	3133.135	4	Os	2543.804	10
Dy	3220.46	10	Hf II	3133.10	5	V I	2543.728	12
Ce	3220.402	12s	Sc II	3133.096	2	Gd	2543.71	2
Th	3220.304	12	Gd	3133.092	3	Ru	2543.678	20
Ti I	3220.277	3h	Ir I	3133.086	20	Re	2543.667	20r
			Cb	3133.083	3	Fe	2543.647	700
			Dy	3132.98	6	Zr II	2543.639	2
			Ru	3132.878	60	Mo	2543.611	3
						Ce	2543.536	4
						Mn	2543.452	4

Other sensitive *iridium* lines: 3513.645 and 2849.725.

Ionization Potential, 7.83

	Most Sensitive Lines		Excitation Potential	
			Low	High
	3719.935	I (b)	0.0	3.32
	3581.195	I (a)	0.9	4.30
	3020.64	I	0.0	4.09

Cb	3720.456	5	Sm	3580.906	40
U	3720.394	6	Ta	3580.889	3
Ti I	3720.384	40	Ir I	3580.861	15
Ce	3720.380	2	V I	3580.825	50
Tb	3720.36	8	Ce	3580.779	10
Th	3720.309	15	Tb	3580.63	8
Mo	3720.254	10	Gd	3580.629	5
Pr	3720.222	15	Sm II	3580.586	2
Os I	3720.132	80	Eu	3580.57	3
Th	3719.969	2			
Ce	3719.946	2w	U	3021.22	10
Fe I	3719.935	1000R	Fe I	3021.073	700R
			Ce	3021.038	15
Ba I	3719.93	2	U	3020.92	8d
Ce II	3719.797	15s	Ce	3020.883	15
Tm	3719.72	10	Ru I	3020.882	60
Mo	3719.692	3	Mo	3020.693	5
U	3719.69	1h	Cr I	3020.673	200r
Nd	3719.595	10	Cb	3020.666	5
Mo	3718.553	5	Dy	3020.65	10
Os I	3719.522	40			
Gd	3719.464	40	Fe I	3020.640	1000R
			Co	3029.639	60
			Tb	3020.58	3
Fe I	3581.649	4	U	3020.571	6
W	3581.238	8	Hf	3020.529	15
			Fe I	3020.489	300r
Fe I	3581.195	1000R	Zr II	3020.467	50
Mo	3581.00	2	Tb	3020.29	8
Re I	3580.968	40w	U	3020.242	8
Sc II	3580.927	12	W	3020.214	7
U	3580.922	3	Ca I	3020.15	2

Other sensitive *iron* lines: 3745.564, 3737.133 and 2483.28.

Lanthanum (La)*

Ionization Potential, 5.59

Most Sensitive Lines			Excitation Potential	
			Low	High
4333.734	II	(c)?	0.2	3.02
3988.518	II	(b)	0.4	3.50
3949.106	II	(a)	0.4	3.53
3337.488	II		0.4	4.10

Ce	4334.227	3	U	3988.293	2	Zr II	3337.924	2
Sm II	4334.149	200	Eu	3988.253	10w	Ce	3337.872	10
V I	4334.092	20	Dy	3988.21	4	Th	3337.869	12
Th	4333.942	5	Os	3988.179	50	Ti II	3337.853	12
Pr	4333.913	150	Cb	3988.157	5	Yt I	3337.849	2
Eu	4333.749	6w	U	3988.029	8	V	3337.846	2
Er	4333.748	9	Pr	3988.019	25	Cu I	3337.844	70
La II	4333.734	800	Th	3988.015	50	Ru I	3337.823	60
Dy	4333.72	2	W	3988.007	7	Tm	3337.82	5
Tb	4333.71	4	Yb	3987.994	1000R	Ta	3337.799	100
U	4333.524	5				Er	3337.79	20
Ce	4333.412	4	Cr I	3949.585	5	U	3337.79	12
Nd	4333.394	5	U	3949.516	2	W	3337.682	10
Zr II	4333.262	8	Tb	3949.509	10	Tb	3337.67	15
Gd	4333.248	10	Nd	3949.457	2	Fe	3337.666	125
Nd	4333.217	3	Cb	3949.455	1	Eu	3337.584	2h
Mo	4333.211	10	Ag	3949.44	3	W	3337.505	5
Pr	4333.148	40	Pr	3949.438	150	Ce	3337.502	20
			Ru I	3949.417	10	bh Sr	3337.5	8
Fe	3989.010	15wh	Tb	3949.39	4	Ta	3337.498	35
Ir I	3988.978	4	Ce II	3949.385	20	Th	3337.488	3
Dy	3988.89	5	Cb	3949.328	3			
U	3988.885	12	U	3949.309	2	La II	3337.488	800
Co I	3988.878	2	Tm	3949.27	50			
Th	3988.852	10	Gd	3949.208	10	U	3337.393	3
V I	3988.833	70	Fe	3949.15	4	Re	3337.254	5d
Nd	3988.812	20	Eu	3949.123	25w	Er	3337.25	15
Ta	3988.701	15	Ce	3949.116	6	Cr I	3337.22	10
Zr II	3988.681	15				Ho	3337.20	12
Mn	3988.671	12	La II	3949.106	1000	Co I	3337.172	60
Cr	3988.656	5				Yb	3337.17	25ℓ
U	3988.644	8	U	3948.991	8	Th	3337.16	6
Th	3988.601	10	Th	3948.971	30	Sb	3337.15	2
Eu	3988.583	5	Ce	3948.949	4	Os	3337.138	2
			Ca I	3948.901	40	Dy	3337.12	2
La II	3988.518	1000	Cr	3948.853	25	U	3337.036	10
			Fe	3948.779	150	Ni I	3337.014	6
Ce	3988.518	8h	Eu	3948.779	4			
			Ti I	3948.674	80h			

At the Cabot Spectrographic Laboratory, La 4333 is usually used for the analysis of lanthanum in rocks. La 3949 and La 3988 are probably more sensitive, but general background interference often mars sensitivity.

La 6249.93 is theoretically the most sensitive atom line, but does not appear to have a very high persistence in the arc; cf. Eu, Gd, Sm, and Y.

Other sensitive *lanthanum* lines: 4086.714, 3794.773 and 3790.822.

Ionization Potential, 7.38

Excitation Potential

Most Sensitive Lines			Low	High
4057.820	I	(a)	1.3	4.36
3683.471	I	(b)	1.0	4.32
2833.069	I	(c)	0.0	4.4

Ce II	4058.244	18	Fe I	3684.112	300	Ta	2833.636	300w
Gd I	4058.231	100	Er	3684.014	6	W	2833.628	15
Fe	4058.229	80	Cb	3683.973	2h	Ce	2833.580	2
Pr	4058.19	6	Th	3683.944	3	Fe	2833.40	10
Co I	4058.190	100	W	3683.941	10	Th	3833.339	8
U	4058.16	10	Eu	3683.85	8W	Ce	2833.309	50d
Ti I	4058.144	50	Pr	3683.846	4	Cb	2833.304	1
Ta	4058.136	2	Fe I	3683.616	3	Hf	2833.276	25
La II	4058.085	4	Ru	3683.592	3	Eu	2833.25	10w
Tb	4058.02	2	U	3683.59	2d	U	2833.244	8
bh Sr	4058.0	3	Ir	3683.523	5	Ir	2833.236	7
U	4057.955	1	Sb	3683.481	3	K	2833.14	2h
Mn	4057.950	80	Mn	3683.474	12			
In	4057.866	80	Er	3683.472	25	Pb I	2833.069	500R
V I	4057.825	10	Zn II	3683.471	20			
Th	4057.823	2				Er	2833.061	25
			Pb I	3683.471	300	Zr	2833.061	2
Pb I	4057.820	2000R				Eu	2833.056	3
			Zr I	3683.470	2	Ce	2833.044	3
Er	4057.819	30	Ag	3683.453	4	W	2832.952	10
Zn II	4057.71	80	Ce	3683.393	2	Ce	2832.928	2
Tb	4057.68	2	W	3683.392	8	Ir	2832.774	5
Sm	4057.653	10	Th	3683.332	5	Rh I	2832.769	5
Mg I	4057.632	10w	W	3683.310	8	Ce	2832.753	2
Ti I	4057.624	40	Eu	3683.27	18w	U	2832.645	2
Mo	4057.584	10	Tb	3683.26	15	Ru	2832.625	20
Ce	4057.556	2	Tm	3683.20	10	Ce	2832.568	2
Ho	4057.55	2	Pr	3683.196	3			
W	4057.452	6	V I	3683.126	100			
Mo	4057.438	4	Fe I	3683.058	200			
Hf	4057.43	3	Ta	3683.058	18			
Dy	4057.40	4	Co I	3683.050	200R			
Ni I	4057.347	2	Pt I	3682.983	8			

Pb 4057 is the most sensitive line of lead but has not been in common use because of interference from CN 4216. Lead is volatile, and the comments about the use of Ga 4172 in the presence of alkali metal vapor apply here also. In basic rocks such as *gabbro, diabase,* and *basalt,* Pb 4057 is often just detectable, provided only the alkali-metal-rich fraction of volatiles has been recorded. In these rocks, Mn 4057.95 is also sometimes evident, and a good dispersion is required to resolve this manganese line from Pb 4057.820.

Other sensitive *lead* lines: 3639.580 and 2614.178.

Lithium (Li)

Ionization Potential, 5.37

	Most Sensitive Lines			Excitation Potential	
				Low	High
	6707.844	I	(a)	0.0	1.84
	6103.642	I	(b)	1.8	3.86
	4602.863	I	(b)	1.8	4.52
	3232.61	I	(b)?	0.0	3.82

W	6708.18	20	Tm	4603.42	35	Ce	3232.875	3
V I	6708.17	2	Tm	4603.21	10	Co I	3232.874	60
Co	6707.857	200wh	Sm	4603.116	5	Ti I	3232.791	8
Mo	6707.85	300w	Tb	4602.95	8	Ru I	3232.751	50
Li I	6707.844	3000R	V I	4602.946	7	Ce	3232.665	3
			Fe I	4602.944	300	W	3232.652	9
Ru	6707.524	5	Gd	4602.944	10	Dy	3232.652	15
Sm II	6707.45	50d	Th	4602.884	5	Sm	3232.620	10
Sm	6707.1	2	Li I	4602.863	800	Li I	3232.61	1000R
Sm	6706.85	5	Cb	4602.860	2	Os	3232.540	150
Nd	6104.106	3	Ru I	4602.808	15	Rh I	3232.504	6
Sm	6103.95	2	Ce	4602.752	4	Sb I	3232.499	150
Sm	6103.723	4	Hf	4602.713	6	Sm	3232.497	4
Dy	6103.67	2	bh La	4602.7	3	W	3232.486	9
Li I	6103.642	2000R	Eu	4602.63	15w	Pb	3232.353	30
			Lu	4602.60	3h	Pd I	3232.32	2
Cb	6103.49	6	Zr I	4602.573	12	Eu	3232.31	4w
Sm	6103.374	30	Pr	4602.562	10	Th	3232.308	8
Dy	6103.370	2	Tb	4602.503	4	Ce	3232.290	15
Fe I	6103.185	8h	Nd	4602.242	10	Ti II	3232.280	30
Ce	6102.751	3				Ta	3232.279	25
Co	6102.739	10	Fe	3233.054	100	W	3232.231	3
Ca I	6102.721	80	Ni I	3232.963	300R	U	3232.157	12
						W	3232.134	6

Co 6707.857 and Mo 6707.85 are listed as relatively intense lines of these two elements but are probably nonexistent. Ca 6102.721 is emitted from many rocks, particularly basic types, and soils, and if prism optics are used, this line interferes with Li 6103.642. In *mica*, a favorite host mineral of lithium, such interference is absent or negligible. Lithium is considerably more volatile than calcium, and interference is minimized by recording only the early period of arcing.

If the far red region of the spectrum is photographed, Li 8126.52 may be employed; it is slightly less sensitive from Li 6103 and is free from interference, except halation from Na $\begin{cases} 8194 \\ 8183 \end{cases}$.

In the ultraviolet, either Li 4602.863 or Li 3232.61 may be employed. Fe 4602.944 is emitted with moderate intensity in almost all rocks and soils, and in many minerals. In *muscovite*, but not *biotite*, Li 4603 is usually free from such interference, provided only the early period of arcing is recorded: lithium is much more volatile than iron.

Fe 3233.054 and Ti 3232.280 are emitted from many rocks and soils, but in most spectrographs these lines are resolved from Li 3232.61.

Another sensitive *lithium* line: 8126.52.

Ionization Potential, 5

Most Sensitive Lines			Excitation Potential
4518.57	I	(c)?	
3077.60	II	(c)?	
2911.39	II	(b)	
2615.42	II	(a)	

Pr	4519.115	3	Ce	3077.644	15	U	2911.287	3
bh Ca	4519.1	3	Fe	3077.643	60	Sm	2911.272	15
Hf	4519.031	1	Lu II	3077.60	100	Re I	2911.231	8
Dy	4518.968	2				Cu I	2911.215	2h
Os	4518.889	15	Ru	3077.552	30	Cr I	2911.145	40
Ti I	4518.697	30	W	3077.519	2	Ce	2911.120	2
Pr	4518.687	2	Cb	3077.443	1	U	2911.104	6
Eu	4518.68	8w	Os	3077.437	80	Fe	2911.08	3
Mo	4518.668	4h	Eu	3077.353	30	Er	2911.069	4s
Th	4518.647	2	Ce	3077.334	15	V II	2911.064	30
Er	4518.640	40w	U	3077.331	4	Fe	2911.01	3
Cr	4518.628	6	Ta	3077.245	150w	W	2911.001	10
U	4518.590	1	Fe II	3077.168	1	Fe	2910.92	10
Lu I	4518.57	300	Yt II	3077.14	7			
			Gd	3077.093	5	Ce	2615.877	4
Dy	4518.538	6				Fe	2615.87	3
Mo	4518.440	5	Mo	2911.915	30	W	2615.695	1
Hf	4518.294	10	Tm	2911.87	4	Re	2615.681	10
Ce	4518.280	4	Tb	2911.81	5	Ta	2615.656	50
Tb	4518.208	2	Mo	2911.765	5	Ta	2615.465	50
U	4518.078	1	U	2911.764	3	Ce	2615.453	5
Ti I	4518.032	100	Cb	2911.745	8	W II	2615.445	6
			Sm	2911.712	6	Fe	2615.422	25
Os	3078.113	125	V	2911.655	1			
Fe	3078.018	100	U	2911.548	12	Lu II	2615.42	100
Ir	3077.882	?h	Yb	2911.52	5	Er	2615.420	15ℓ
V	3077.853	5h	Ce	2911.514	8	Mo	2615.391	25
Cr I	3077.831	25	Er	2911.417	30	Co I	2615.335	10
U	3077.730	2				Yb	2615.26	3
Os	3077.720	100	Lu II	2911.39	100	Ta	2615.250	40
V I	3077.718	10				W	2615.122	10
Mo	3077.661	20	Os	2911.341	5	U	2615.120	2
Ir I	3077.648	8	Th	2911.324	8	Ru	2615.093	60
						Ir I	2614.984	25

Other sensitive *lutetium* lines: 3507.39 and 3359.56.

Magnesium (Mg)

Ionization Potential, 7.61

	Most Sensitive Lines		Excitation Potential	
			Low	High
	5183.618	I	2.7	5.09
	3838.258	I (b)	2.7	5.92
	2852.129	I (a)	0.0	4.3

Yb	5184.181	8	Eu	3838.36	2w	Eu	2852.56	5W
Ru	5184.034	4	Pr	3838.341	5	V	2852.536	6
Th	5183.986	6	Er	3838.339	10	Ag	2852.53	1
W	5183.972	20	Nd	3838.33	40	Th	2852.502	2h
La I	5183.923	25	Ca	3838.318	2	Ir	2852.479	2
Pr	5183.848	5	Zr II	3838.283	10	U	3852.469	6
Cb	5183.82	5h				Re	2852.399	10
Ti I	5183.72	8	Mg I	3838.258	300	Ta	2852.355	5
Zr I	5183.705	6	Mn	3838.247	10	Fe	2852.35	2
Mg I	5183.618	500wh	Eu	3838.24	4	Ce	2852.237	3
Co	5183.610	35	Tm	3838.204	80	Mo	2852.131	10h
Eu	5183.606	4	Li I	3838.15	5	Ir	2852.131	20
La II	5183.422	300	U	3838.150	8			
Cb	5183.33	5h	Ru I	3838.067	12	Mg I	2852.129	300R
Ce	5183.197	10	Fe	3838.036	1			
Nd	5182.603	8	Nd	3837.909	10	Dy	2852.129	5
			Mo	3837.882	3	Ce	2852.124	50d
			Eu	3837.88	6w	W	2852.10	1d
Ru	3838.728	10	Th	3837.880	10	Hf II	2852.012	20
Nd	3838.724	50	Dy	3837.86	2	Cb	2851.977	4
Dy	3838.67	10	V	3837.852	5	Zr II	2851.967	12
Os I	3838.59	3	Tb	3837.83	8	Fe I	2851.798	200
Ce	3838.542	35				V I	2851.748	30
W	3838.504	15	Na I	2852.828	100R	Mg I	2851.65	25
Hf II	3838.37	2	U	2852.750	15			

*Under ordinary working conditions no iron line appears at λ2852.13 A.

Other sensitive *magnesium* lines: 3838.258, 2802.695 and 2795.53.

Ionization Potential, 7.41

	Most Sensitive Lines			Excitation Potential	
				Low	High
	4034.490	I	(aaa)	0.0	3.06
	4033.073	I	(aa)	0.0	3.06
	4030.755	I	(a)	0.0	3.06
	2576.104	II	(b)	0.0	4.8

Sm II	4035.101	50	Pr	4033.24	3	Ta	4030.668	10
Cb	4035.098	4	Cb	4033.203	5	Eu	4030.66	5w
Pr	4035.07	2	Sr I	4033.191	6	Sc I	4030.657	10
Cr	4034.998	8				Ti I	4030.514	80
Ti I	4034.910	25	Mn I	4033.073	400r	Fe I	4030.492	120
Th	4034.886	8	Cr	4033.072	15	Nd	4030.470	20
Co	4034.858	2	Ta	4033.069	100	Sm II	4030.425	10
Tm	4034.74	10	In	4033.066	4	Sr I	4030.377	40
Ce	4034.570	2	Tb	4033.04	125	Ce II	4030.344	18
Cb	4034.523	10	Ga I	4032.982	1000R	Ca	4030.3	10
Mn I	4034.490	250r	Sm	4032.977	20	Th	4030.293	8
Gd	4034.38	5	Pr	4032.974	15	Eu	4030.203	10w
Pr	4034.30	20	V I	4032.856	2			
Ce	4034.259	2	Dy	4032.847	8			
Th	4034.256	10	Ce	4032.748	2	Cb	2576.597	3
Sc I	4034.23	8	Tb	4032.705	3	Mo	2576.563	2
Nd	4034.147	10d	Ti I	4032.632	35	V	2576.480	1
Eu	4034.11	2	Fe I	4032.630	80	W II	2576.360	2
Zr II	4034.086	5				Th	2576.336	6
Cr I	4034.048	20	V I	4031.219	10	Re	2576.319	15
Nd	4034.012	4	Cr	4031.130	30	Hg I	2576.295	20
U	4034.002	4	Th	4031.099	5	Rh	2576.229	2
Mo	4033.999	3	Pr	4031.09	12	W	2576.165	2
Ti I	4033.906	40	Dy	4031.081	7	Zr I	2576.105	8
			Ru I	4030.997	15	Mn II	2576.104	300R
			Mo	4030.915	3	Co	2576.104	30
Zr	4033.584	3	Gd	4030.881	8	Cb	2575.963	1
Sb	4033.543	70	Th	4030.855	10	Ce	2575.933	6
Nd	4033.504	10	Ce	4030.853	2	W	2575.897	9
Gd	4033.491	10	Yt	4030.83	2	Rh I	2575.75	2
U	4033.427	12	Zr I	4030.759	20	Ag	2575.744	10h
Ce	4033.378	2h	U	4030.758	5	Fe	2575.744	80
Re I	4033.307	40	Mn I	4030.755	500r	Ir I	2575.743	10
Cr I	4033.263	30	Cr	4030.681	40	Mn	2575.509	150

The group at λ 4030 A tends to have interference from CN 4216, and for highest sensitivity, such emission should be as low as possible. Interference from Ga 4032.982 with Mn 4033.073 is omnipresent in almost all rocks, soils, and silicate minerals.

Other sensitive *manganese* lines: 2593.729 and 2605.688.

Mercury (Hg)

Ionization Potential, 10.38

	Most Sensitive Lines		Excitation Potential	
			Low	High
	4358.35 I		4.9	7.7
	2536.519 I (b)		0.0	4.9

Th	4358.832	3	Rh	2537.039	15
Tb	4358.77	2	Lu	2536.95	10
Zr I	4358.742	10	V	2536.926	10
Ho	4358.74	3	Mo	2536.849	25
Yt II	4358.726	60	Fe II	2536.817	10
Nd	4358.699	15	U	2536.794	4
Re I	4358.688	80	Tb	2536.75	3
U	4358.654	2	Rh	2536.706	15
Ta	4358.654	10	Fe II	2536.673	1
Sc I	4358.645	10	Ta	2536.67	2h
Pd I	4358.599	25	Ir	2536.665	3
Th	4358.556	4	W	2536.605	1
Mo	4358.551	20w	U	2536.600	3
Fe I	4358.505	70	Bi	2536.56	5h
Dy	4358.461	25	Th	2536.558	5
Tb	4358.43	3			
Hg I	4358.35	3000w	Hg I	2536.519	2000R
Pt I	4358.336	2	Co I	2536.493	1
Th	4358.333	3	Pt I	2536.487	100
Ir	4358.279	8	U	2536.238	4
Er	4358.172	4	Ta	2536.227	100W
Nd	4358.169	50	Fe	2536.224	3
Os	4358.141	9	Ru	2536.216	12
Ta	4358.033	3	Ir	2536.127	2
Os	4357.980	12	W	2535.988	4
Re	4357.97	15			
La I	4357.917	5			
Ce	4357.907	12			

Mercury is detectable in some *sphalerite* specimens by using Hg 2536.519, which, however, must be used with caution because of interference from Co 2536.493 above about 0.1% (Oftedal, 1941).

Theoretically Hg 1849 is the most sensitive atom line, but this wavelength is below the normally usable range.

Another sensitive *mercury* line: 3650.146.

Ionization Potential, 7.35

Most Sensitive Lines		Excitation Potential	
Most Sensitive Lines		Low	High
3902.963	I (a)	0.0	3.16
3798.252	I (aa)	0.0	3.25
3170.347	I (b)	0.0	3.89

Nd	3903.510	10	Tm	3798.76	20	Hf II	3797.923	25
Sm	3903.412	60	Eu	3798.71	2wh	Th	3797.91	2
Ce	3903.342	15	Ir I	3798.666	5	Nd	3797.89	20d
Dy	3903.332	8	Hf	3798.662	5	U	3797.773	10
W	3903.298	6	V I	3798.661	7			
U	3903.262	10	Dy	3798.65	2			
V II	3903.262	3	Er	3798.65	4	U	3170.855	10
Eu	3903.240	10W	Ce	3798.624	3	Dy	3170.746	10
Cr I	3903.164	35	Tb	3798.59	15	Ni I	3170.715	4
Ce	3903.120	2	Tm	3798.55	15	Ag	3170.579	5
Tb	3903.11	3	Fe I	3798.513	400	U	3170.538	3
Th	3903.093	15	Ce	3798.51	3	Ce	3170.528	2
			Yb	3798.44	4	Th	3170.429	10
Mo I	3902.963	1000R	Ti I	3798.314	10	Eu	3170.38	15
Fe I	3902.948	500	Ir	3798.272	8			
Cr I	3902.915	100	Er	3798.25	5	Mo	3170.347	1000R
Ce	3902.89	8	U	3798.259	2	Fe II	3170.346	10
Ir I	3902.849	8				Ta	3170.289	250w
Re	3902.821	3	Mo I	3798.252	1000R	Sm II	3170.203	15
Ru	3902.816	5	Ce	3798.238	2	W	3170.201	15
Er	3902.766	10	Yb	3798.17	4	Cb	3170.160	2
Ce	3902.745	2	Cb	3798.121	50	Ru	3170.093	30
Gd I	3902.717	25	Th	3798.103	5	U	3170.09	2
W	3902.684	5	Ce	3798.08	2	Ce	3170.069	12
Ir I	3902.662	8	Ir	3798.059	6	Nd	3170.015	10
Re	3902.583	6	Ru I	3798.052	30	U	3169.989	6
La I	3902.576	20	Fe I	3797.949	4	Dy	3169.978	100
U	3902.561	18	Tb	3797.93	15	W	3169.928	10
V I	3902.558	6	Ir	3797.924	2	Tm	3169.89	15
Ce	3902.509	3				Sm II	3169.870	25
Ir I	3902.506	10				Ca I	3169.854	10
Pr	3902.470	60						

The most sensitive line, Mo 3798, is rarely used if carbon or graphite electrodes are employed, because of excessive interference from intense CN 3883; this statement applies also to Mo 3864. In almost all rocks, minerals, and soils, intense Fe 3902.948 interferes excessively with Mo 3902.963.

Mo 3170 is considerably less sensitive, but appears free from interference and has been successfully used, particularly by Mitchell and co-workers (Macaulay Institute of Soils Research) for the analysis of molybdenum in some rocks (mainly granitelike types).

Other sensitive *molybdenum* lines: 3864.110, 3193.973 and 2816.154.

Neodymium (Nd)*

Ionization Potential, 6.3

Most Sensitive Lines			Excitation Potential	
			Low	High
4303.573	II	(a)?	0.0	2.87
4247.367	II		0.0	2.91
4061.085	II	(b)?	0.5	3.5
4012.250	II	(b)?	0.6	3.70

Tb	4304.02	12	Pr	4061.336	4
Mo	4304.020	12	Gd	4061.298	8
Ti	4303.961	8	Cb	4061.263	4
Cb	4303.881	3	Gd	4061.164	3
Er	4303.813	12	Fe	4061.110	3
Dy	4303.60	3	Nd II	4061.085	40
Hf	4303.596	10			
Pr	4303.594	100	Er	4061.082	5
Fe	4303.585	25	Sr I	4061.06	8
Nd II	4303.573	100	Dy	4061.054	3
			Sm II	4061.049	8
Ta	4303.54	1	Au II	4060.99	3
W	4303.533	4	U	4060.907	4
V	4303.527	15	Tb	4060.86	25
Gd	4303.456	6	V I	4060.85	2
U	4303.325	6	Cb	4060.787	10
Co I	4303.236	15	U	4060.768	6
Fe II	4303.168	12	Cr	4060.765	12
Pr	4303.139	20	Ce	4060.716	8
			W	4060.708	8
Eu	4247.831	5h	Dy	4060.58	8
Eu	4247.73	8	Zr I	4060.579	10
Ce	4247.695	2	Nd	4060.562	10
Re	4247.694	3			
Cb	4247.690	2	Nd	4012.704	15
Pr	4247.662	60	Er	4012.58	4
Ce	4247.653	2	Dy	4012.523	4
Th	4247.599	8	Mo	4012.51	3
Fe I	4247.433	200	Th	4012.497	15
U	4247.430	5	Cr	4012.469	70
Sm II	4247.395	15	Tb	4012.45	5
Nd II	4247.367	50	Ti II	4012.391	35
			Ce I,II	4012.388	60
Dy	4247.36	30	Mo	4012.270	3
U	4247.136	10	Re	4012.260	25
Eu	4247.069	15	Er	4012.253	12
Ce	4246.938	3	Zr I	4012.252	20
P	4246.88	70	Nd II	4012.250	80
Nd	4246.879	10			
			U	4012.161	6
Tb	4061.57	40	Co I	4012.160	2
Eu	4061.552	12	Ce	4012.139	40
Zr I	4061.529	25	Ta	4012.111	5h
Ce II	4061.423	6	Mo	4011.966	25
Ta	4061.399	50	Hf	4011.944	3
U	4061.349	12	Mn	4011.905	12

*See list of sensitive rare earth lines at end of tables.

In the Cabot Spectrographic Laboratory, Nd 4303.573 has been found a satisfactory line for the determination of neodymium in granitelike rocks. It must be used with much caution, however, because in almost all rocks (particularly basic types) and soils, there is emission from an iron line of like wavelength (not listed in the M.I.T. tables and hence not given above) which has an intensity of about "25," based on the M.I.T. scale.

Nd 4247.367 frequently has interference from Fe 4247.433 and even in granitelike rocks this interference is excessive.

Nd 4012 is liable to interference from titanium and cerium lines in rocks and soils.

Other sensitive *neodymium* lines: 4156.083 and 4109.455.

Ionization Potential, 7.61

	Most Sensitive Lines			Excitation Potential	
				Low	High
	3524.541	I	(b)	0.03	3.53
	3492.956	I	(b)	0.1	3.64
	3414.765	I	(a)	0.03	3.64

Sm	3525.065	2	Sm II	3493.408	2	Dy	3492.52	2
Ba I	3524.985	20	Eu	3493.407	7	Ce	3492.486	5
Mo	3524.981	5	U	3493.407	2			
Cb	3524.936	2	Mo	3493.337	6			
Dy	3524.92	6	U	3493.333	6	Ir	3415.241	10
Er	3524.920	20	Fe I	3493.290	1	Os	3415.224	5
Ru I	3524.902	12	Ti I	3493.280	15	Th	3415.13	2
V II	3524.715	10	Tb	3493.27	8	Tb	3415.12	8
W	3524.681	7	Dy	3493.26	3	Pr	3415.079	4
Mo	3524.646	5	Ru	3493.220	20	Ce	3415.069	8
Dy	3524.61	6	W	3493.195	6	Sm II	3414.953	10
Ni I	3524.541	1000R	V II	3493.167	15	Zr I	3414.950	2
			Pr	3493.158	10	Ho	3414.92	30
Mn	3524.540	15	Ce	3493.110	12	Dy	3414.830	35
Sm	3524.538	10	Ho	3493.10	10	Er	3414.79	8
Zr I	3524.538	9	W	3493.036	5	Eu	3414.773	40
Pr	3524.47	3	Tb	3492.99	15	Pr	3414.767	7
Ir	3524.372	2h	Ce	3492.983	3	Ce	3414.766	5
Eu	3524.34	3w	Eu	3492.969	2	Ni I	3414.765	1000R
W	3524.246	9	Tb	3492.96	15			
Zr	3524.242	12	Mn	3492.960	10	Co I	3414.736	200W
Fe I	3524.241	60	Ni I	3492.956	1000R	Zr II	3414.661	20
Ti	3524.240	2				Ru I	3414.642	50
Cu I	3524.239	40	Sm	3492.895	3	U	3414.63	3d
Mo	3524.228	8	Mo	3492.825	3	Ce	3414.605	5
Gd	3524.198	25	U	3492.799	2	Ag I	3414.55	4
Ru	3524.152	6	Sm	3492.775	3	Th	3414.513	6
Ce	3524.073	8	Pr	3492.73	4	Yt	3414.49	3
Fe	3524.071	50	Th	3492.683	2	U	3414.36	8d
			Sm II	3492.622	8	Ce	3414.313	8
			Tm	3492.59	20	Cr	3414.305	8wh
Fe II	3493.474	40	Tb	3492.56	15	Dy	3414.30	2
Cb	3493.473	3	Ce	3492.559	3	Nd	3414.298	10
Ta	3493.465	15W	Er	3492.543	25d	Ru	3414.282	12

In most common rocks and soils, and in many minerals, Ni 3414.765 may be used safely, but in some sulfide minerals with appreciable traces of cobalt, Co 3414.736 interferes.

Other sensitive *nickel* lines: 3515.054 and 3446.263.

Niobium (Nb)

Ionization Potential, 6.77

	Most Sensitive Lines			Excitation Potential	
				Low	High
	4079.729	I	(b)	0.1	3.11
	4058.938	I	(a)	0.1	3.17

Fe I	4080.221	60	Mn	4059.392	20
Cr	4080.221	15	Eu	4059.376	25
bh Sr	4080.1	2	Pr	4059.37	4
Ce	4080.025	5	Ce	4059.367	3
Ir	4079.897	25	Gd	4059.346	10w
U	4079.847	1	Ce II	4059.322	8h
Fe I	4079.845	80	Th	4059.259	8
Sm	4079.829	20	W	4059.254	5
Pr	4079.786	50	Ir	4059.234	30
W	4079.785	4	Eu	4059.035	4
			U	4059.025	1
Cb I	4079.729	500w	Zr I	4058.985	8
Ti I	4079.721	40	Mg	4058.96	2
Ce	4079.667	15			
Th	4079.612	5	Cb I	4058.938	1000w
Dy	4079.595	8	Mn	4058.930	80
Mn	4079.422	50	Ca I	4058.930	3d
Re	4079.363	20	Tm	4058.92	20
Mo	4079.342	4	Ru	4058.882	10
Ru I	4079.277	12	Sm II	4058.867	30
			Tb	4058.81	3W
			Pr	4058.778	25
			Cr	4058.772	80
			Fe I	4058.760	40
			Zr I	4058.624	9
			Co I	4058.600	100
			Ta	4058.464	10

Both Nb 4079.729 and Nb 4058.938 are liable to line interference apart from CN interference from CN 4216. In many rocks and soils, Mn 4079.422, Ti 4079.721, and Fe 4079.845 may be emitted; in most rocks and soils, Mn 4058.930 is emitted.

Other sensitive *niobium* lines: 4123.810, 3194.977, 3130.786 and 3094.183.

Ionization Potential, 8.7

Most Sensitive Lines				Excitation Potential Low	High

				Low	High
3058.66	I	(b)		0.0	4.03
2909.061	I	(a)		0.0	4.2

Ru	3059.169	50	Dy	2909.325	2
Fe I	3059.086	600r	Fe	2909.31	4
Eu	3059.00	20	U	2909.250	6
Tm	3058.99	10	Ru	2909.224	12
U	3058.98	8d	Yb	2909.19	2
Ru I	3058.786	30	W	2909.123	8
Re I	3058.786	50	Mo II	2909.116	25
Os I	3058.66	500R	Os I	2909.061	500R
Ru I	3058.655	30	Cr I	2909.052	60r
Ir	3058.653	5	Eu	2909.01	40
Ta	3058.636	50	Cb	2908.979	1
Mo	3058.597	20	Ta	2908.910	150
Ce	3058.551	12	Cb	2908.881	2
Fe	3058.493	3	Mn	2908.879	10
Th	3058.431	10	U	2908.878	2
Th	3058.142	8	Fe	2908.859	80
			Hf II	2908.858	3
Ir	2909.558	18	V II	2908.817	70r
Fe	2909.503	70	Cd I	2908.74	5l
Yb	2909.48	2	Tm	2908.69	5
Ho	2909.42	40	Er	2908.535	6

Other sensitive *osmium* lines: 3267.94, 3262.290 and 2488.548.

Palladium (Pd)

Ionization Potential, 8.33

	Most Sensitive Lines		Excitation Potential	
			Low	High
	3421.24 I (b)		1.0	4.62
	3404.580 I (a)		0.8	4.44

Cr	3421.72	12	Dy	3420.81	5
Ce	3421.714	3	Mn	3420.795	8
U	3421.69	8	Co I	3420.792	80
Os	3421.687	30	Re I	3420.758	40
Eu	3421.667	5	Ni I	3420.741	30
Cr	3421.64	2h			
Ho	3421.64	20	Ti I	3405.094	20
Co I	3421.626	20	Ag	3405.03	3
Re	3421.579	15	Dy	3404.99	4
Ce II	3421.542	5	V I	3404.960	8
Ba I	3421.48	2	U	3404.933	3
Hf II	3421.45	3	Ce	3404.910	18
Zr I	3421.419	3	Mo	3404.864	6
U	3421.38	8d	Zr II	3404.832	40
Co I	3421.348	3	W	3404.803	8
Ni I	3421.342	30	Sm	3404.767	2
Dy	3421.32	7	Nd	3404.763	4
Sm	3421.297	2	Fe I	3404.754	2
Mo	3421.250	6	Re I	3404.724	100
			Tb	3404.71	3
Pd I	3421.24	2000R	Th	3404.654	4
Cr II	3421.212	50			
Ta	3421.212	1	Pd I	3404.580	2000R
Ni I	3421.204	4	La I	3404.52	9
Th	3421.189	10	Ce	3404.428	12
Cb	3421.162	10w	Fe I	3404.359	100
W	3421.134	3d	Mo	3404.342	20
Pr	3421.112	10	Fe I	3404.304	25
Ce	3421.071	6	Tb	3404.24	15
Er	3421.065	9	W	3404.224	8
Ba I	3421.01	3	Ta	3404.163	5
Ce	3420.955	5	Er	3404.13	8

Other sensitive *palladium* lines: 3634.695 and 3242.71.

Ionization Potential, 11.1

	Most Sensitive Lines		Excitation Potential	
			Low	High
	2554.93	I		2.3	7.1
	2553.28	I		2.3	7.1
	2535.65	I (b)		2.3	7.2
	2534.01	I		2.3	7.2

Fe II	2555.442	2	Ce	2553.588	2	Th	2535.870	5
Mo	2555.42	3	Cd I	2553.56	25	**P I**	**2535.65**	**100**
Rh I	2555.360	100	Re	2553.556	5			
Ir I	2555.347	25	Fe	2553.50	2	Fe I	2535.604	1000
Cb	2555.319	1	Cb	2553.492	1	Ta	2535.598	50h
Os	2555.273	10	Ce	2553.456	2	Fe	2535.364	1
Fe	2555.220	10	Ag II	2553.407	2	W	2535.332	8
U	2555.210	4	Ni I	2553.377	20	Ag II	2535.307	10
W	2555.205	10	Co I	2553.374	10r	Zr II	2535.15	1
W II	2555.091	10	Ce	2553.344	3			
Fe II	2555.066	20	Ru	2553.310	6	Cb	2534.441	1
Ta	2555.052	50	**P I**	**2553.28**	**80**	Fe II	2534.416	7
Re	2554.931	15				Cr II	2534.336	8
P I	**2554.93**	**60**	Fe	2553.185	10	V I	2534.259	2
			Ta	2553.181	10h	Ce	2534.180	2
Ta	2554.907	50h	W	2553.162	12	Os	2534.166	8
W II	2554.862	15	Cr I	2553.062	20	Ta	2534.162	3
V I	2554.862	15	Zr II	2553.047	2	W	2534.146	2
Cb	2554.795	1	V	2553.024	7	Re	2534.101	10
Eu	2554.785	10	Co I	2553.003	40r	Rh	2534.072	4
Ru	2554.687	8	Ti	2552.98	10R	**P I**	**2534.01**	**50**
W	2554.668	4	V	2552.962	10			
Re	2554.631	5	Mo	2552.873	20	Ir I	2534.006	2
Ta	2554.622	50	Fe I	2552.832	5	Ru	2534.001	4
Mg I	2554.62	4	Fe	2552.773	20	W	2533.982	10
Sb	2554.617	30				V	2533.963	1
Fe	2554.520	2				Cb	2533.920	1
Cd I	2554.51	3	Ir	2536.127	2	Cd I	2533.91	2
Os	2554.465	20	W	2535.988	4	Co	2533.81	5r
Ir I	2554.399	15	Ni	2535.967	25	V	2533.805	10
			Pt	2535.967	25	U	2533.804	4
U	2553.73	3	Co I	2535.964	10r	Fe	2533.803	12
Mo	2553.698	15	Ta	2535.96	4	W	2533.633	10
V	2553.669	10	U	2535.90	5	Fe II	2533.627	8
W	2553.598	10	Ti II	2535.871	20	Rh	2533.591	2

Excessive interference from Fe 2535.604 with P 2535.65 is present in almost all rock types, soils, and most minerals.

According to theory, the most sensitive atom line is P 1774.9, which, however, is below the wavelength range normally used.

Platinum (Pt)

Ionization Potential, 8.96

Most Sensitive Lines			Excitation Potential	
			Low	High
3064.712	I		0.0	4.03
2659.454	I	(a)	0.0	4.6

U	3065.198	6	Al	3064.304	20
Dy	3065.14	4	Mo	3064.279	80
Sc II	3065.106	12d	Fe	3064.217	4
Cr	3065.067	20			
Yb	3065.048	4	Ir I	2659.946	2
Mo	3065.042	30	Ga	2659.866	5
Sm	3065.008	4	Th	2659.86	3
Er	3064.97	3	Os	2659.833	30
W	3064.937	10s	Re	2659.792	15
Yb	3064.91	2	Ce	2659.716	2
U	3064.908	1	Ta	2659.655	15
Er	3064.84	7	Ru I	2659.615	80
Ru	3064.838	70	V	2659.606	9
Ir I	3064.790	5	bh C	2659.6	20
			Rh I	2659.472	3
Pt I	3064.712	2000R			
			Pt I	2659.454	2000R
Hf II	3064.68	10			
Zr II	3064.634	5	Eu	2659.42	4
Ni I	3064.623	200r	Ta	2659.41	20
Re	3064.600	20	Yb	2659.28	2
U	3064.591	4	Fe	2659.24	8
Mo	3064.555	15	Ir	2659.144	4
Cb	3064.533	5w	Cb	2659.052	3h
Ir I	3064.509	20	U	2659.025	8
Na II	3064.372	2	Re	2659.023	25
Co I	3064.370	100	Rh I	2659.011	2

Platinum is not directly detectable in rocks, soils and silicate minerals. In basic rocks and mafic minerals, emission at λ 3064 is due to Ni 3064.623. In a few sulfide minerals, platinum may be detectable. These sometimes contain appreciable concentrations of nickel, which sometimes causes emission of Ni 3064; the use of Pt 2659 is therefore recommended.

Other sensitive *platinum* lines: 2997.967 and 2830.295.

Ionization Potential, 4.32

Most Sensitive Lines			Excitation Potential	
			Low	High
7698.979	I	(a)	0.0	1.60
7664.907	I	(aa)	0.0	1.61
4047.201	I	(b)	0.0	3.05
4044.140	I	(bb)	0.0	3.05

Yb	7699.49	2000	Mo	4047.398	4	Tm	4044.47	15
Ta	7699.14	5	Ce	4047.392	4	Ca	4044.419	5d
K I	7698.979	5000R	Sm II	4047.363	8	U	4044.416	18
			Ca	4047.351	2	Hf	4044.39	10
Nd	7698.94	2h	Ir	4047.329	4	Nd	4044.347	3
Yt	7698.00	4	Fe I	4047.310	3	Ce	4044.330	4h
Sc I	7697.73	20	Ce	4047.275	18	W	4044.288	15
			Mo	4047.204	4	K I	4044.140	800
Dy	7666.78	2	K I	4047.201	400	Sm	4044.113	4
bh Ti	7666.4	6	Tb	4047.16	9	Cb	4044.105	5
Sc I	7665.72	5	Nd	4047.158	12	Hg II	4044.10	5
K I	7664.907	9000R	Pr	4047.098	20	Ce	4044.062	3
			Gd	4047.093	6	U	4044.041	1
Cu II	7664.70	5	U	4047.05	6	Gd	4044.030	3h
La I	7664.34	8	Er	4046.960	8	Eu	4043.97	20
Fe I	7664.302	15	Mo	4046.886	3	Ce	4043.955	3
			Ce	4046.853	3	Fe I	4043.905	25
			Gd	4046.842	10	Sc I	4043.804	12
Yt I	4047.632	50	Ni I	4046.761	2	Ti I	4043.775	20
Ce	4047.620	3	Cr I	4046.760	30	Ce	4043.747	3
U	4047.610	18				Mo	4043.738	8
Mo	4047.563	4	Fe I	4044.611	70	Gd	4043.710	5
Ho	4047.50	3	Zr I	4044.564	25	Cr	4043.696	30

CN emission must be reduced for highest sensitivity from K $\begin{cases} 4044 \\ 4047 \end{cases}$ because of interference from CN 4216. This may be done as described for gallium; see Ahrens, 1950, Chap. 10. Fe 4045.815 is an intense iron line which may cause halation interference, particularly in basic rocks, unless only the early period of arcing is recorded, preferably at a low amperage (3 amp): iron is less volatile than potassium.

Praseodymium (Pr)

Ionization Potential, 5.8

Most Sensitive Lines			Excitation Potential	
			Low	High
4225.327	II	(b)?	0.0	2.92
4179.422	II	(a)?	0.2	3.16
4222.98	II	(b)?	0.05	2.98
3908.431	II	(a)?	0.0	3.16

Gd	4225.853	150	Mo	4222.961	15	Cb	3908.973	10
U	4225.75	1	U	4222.94	1	Ni I	3908.931	2
Ce	4225.746	6	Tb	4222.91	6W	Ir	3908.834	5
Sc I	4225.58	4	Ce	4222.884	3	Ce	3908.765	12
Nd	4225.556	3	Na I	4222.8	3	Ru	3908.765	12
Ir	4225.496	15	U	4222.739	6	Cr I	3908.755	200
Fe I	4225.465	80	Cr I	4222.732	100	U	3908.682	2
Zr I	4225.463	6	Tb	4222.71	9	Tb	3908.66	4
U	4225.369	8	Tm	4222.67	10	Cb	3908.594	3
Pr II	4225.327	50	Ce	4222.599	80	Ce I,II	3908.543	20
Sm II	4225.318	40	Mo	4222.411	20	Th	3908.488	3
Gd	4225.264	3				U	3908.473	8
Zr I	4225.263	4	Ti I	4179.885	4	Pr II	3908.431	100
Mo	4225.248	5	Zr II	4179.809	15			
V II	4225.225	3	Ce	4179.806	1	Er	3908.418	10
Dy	4225.153	40	Tb	4179.80	6	Ce	3908.408	30
Gd	4225.148	20	Cb	4179.755	10	U	3908.331	10
Ho	4225.13	3	Re	4179.75	2h	V	3908.317	50
Co	4225.109	5	Th	4179.718	8	Sm	3908.258	6
Ru	4225.092	25	U	4179.634	2	Mo	3908.249	5
Gd I	4225.028	15	Nd	4179.585	10	Re	3908.202	25
Mo	4224.929	5	Hf II	4179.53	5	Mn	3908.162	3
Eu	4224.88	4	Cu II	4179.508	1h	Gd	3908.146	5
Tb	4224.85	5	Dy	4179.46	3	Ce II	3908.094	8
Nd	4224.847	15	U	4179.432	10	Tb	3908.076	20
Ti I	4224.793	40	Pr II	4179.422	200	Pr	3908.033	100
			V I	4179.419	20	Ce	3907.964	2
Cr I	4223.470	15	Er	4179.401	5	Fe	3907.937	100
Dy	4223.38	2	Eu	4179.40	2			
Tb	4223.32	10	Ba	4179.372	6			
U	4223.30	1h	Ce II	4179.289	10			
Nd	4223.208	15	Cr	4179.257	100			
Ir	4223.159	15	Co I	4179.229	15			
Ce	4223.153	3	Ce	4179.079	8			
Lu	4223.09	1	U	4179.001	15			
Sm	4223.056	3	Tb	4178.97	50d			
Gd	4222.98	10	Fe II	4178.868	10			
Pr II	4222.98	125						

Another sensitive *praseodymium* line: 4100.746.

Ionization Potential, 7.85

Most Sensitive Lines			Excitation Potential	
			Low	High
4889.17	I	(b)	0.0	2.52
3460.47	I	(a)	0.0	3.57

Pr	4889.663	5	Sc I	3460.700	6
Ce	4889.587	20	Pr	3460.663	3
Cb	4889.557	3	Dy	3460.64	4
Dy	4889.325	5	Sm	3460.63	3w
Mo	4889.216	25	Ce	3460.581	2
Gd	4889.203	60	Nd	3460.581	25
			Ir	3460.544	3
Re I	4889.17	2000w			
Nd	4889.106	8	Re I	3460.47	1000W
Fe I	4889.009	2wh	Cr I	3460.430	40
Er	4888.874	3	Dy	3460.40	20
Fe I	4888.651	2	Tb	3460.38	15
Ru	4888.607	6	U	3460.351	3
Cr I	4888.530	100	Mn II	3460.328	60
			La II	3460.31	2
			Eu	3460.290	15
Er	3460.968	20𝑙	Yb	3460.27	30
Ho	3460.95	6	Mo	3460.226	5
W	3460.784	3	Ce	3460.163	6
Mo	3460.784	25	Nd	3460.13	6
Ce	3460.783	2	U	3460.058	5
U	3460.781	2	Dy	3460.05	5
Pd I	3460.774	300r	Mn II	3460.018	5
Co I	3460.719	18	Zr II	3459.933	20

Other sensitive *rhenium* lines: 3451.808 and 3464.722.

Rhodium (Rh)

Ionization Potential, 7.7

	Most Sensitive Lines		Excitation Potential	
			Low	High
	3692.357	I (b)	0.0	3.34
	3434.893	I (a)	0.0	3.59

Mn	3692.812	50	Ti	3435.432	10
Nd	3692.768	12	Dy	3435.27	4
Sm	3692.763	20	Sm II	3435.256	5
U	3692.750	10	Os	3435.256	20
W	3692.725	7	W	3435.243	6
Ir I	3692.694	15	Ce	3435.207	20
Eu	3692.66	5w	Eu	3435.205	35
Er	3692.652	20	U	3435.200	10
Fe	3692.652	5	Ru I	3435.186	60
Ho	3692.65	10	Eu	3435.064	12
Mo	3692.645	3	Tb	3434.92	30
Zr II	3692.635	2			
Th	3692.571	10	Rh	3434.893	1000r
Ce	3692.552	2	Hf	3434.89	5
Yt I	3692.529	7	Os	3434.889	20
Ru	3692.370	6	U	3434.805	2h
			Mo	3434.790	50
Rh I	3692.357	500hd	Th	3434.762	8
Pr	3692.293	4	Ir I	3434.757	10
V I	3692.225	200R	Pr	3434.757	20
Ce	3692.222	3	Eu	3434.74	3
Sm II	3692.221	90	Ag I	3434.646	2h
Eu	3692.22	4wh	Er	3434.634	12
Ir	3692.20	2	U	3434.614	12
Ti	3692.134	12	Yb	3434.61	5
Re	3692.126	15	Tb	3434.54	15
Mo	3692.081	5	Ta	3434.500	35
Th	3692.080	8	Mo	3434.496	5
U	3692.052	4	Pr	3434.486	3
Tb	3692.02	15	Dy	3434.373	80
Eu	3691.98	3W			
U	3691.917	6			
Th	3691.881	8			

Other sensitive *rhodium* lines: 3657.987 and 3396.85.

Ionization Potential, 4.16

	Most Sensitive Lines	Excitation Potential	
		Low	High
7947.60	I (a)	0.0	1.55
7800.227	I (aa)	0.0	1.58
4215.556	I (b)	0.0	2.93
4201.851	I (bb)	0.0	2.94

Ru I	7948.15	15	U	4215.99	5	V II	4202.34	6
Sm II	7948.12	100d	Pr	4215.98	4	Dy	4202.250	20
Mn	7948.10	2	Fe I	4215.970	2	Mo	4202.219	5
			E r	4215.964	9	Ni I	4202.154	5
Rb I	7947.60	5000R	Tb	4215.95	3	Os	4202.062	100
						Fe I	4202.031	400
V I	7947.38	8	Rb I	4215.556	1000R	Eu	4202.03	5
Sm II	7947.00	15d				Ta	4201.97	5h
			Tm	4215.53	10	Th	4201.852	8
			Sr II	4215.524	300r	Rb I	4201.851	2000R
Si	7801.30	3h	U	4215.51	3			
Re	7801.05	4	Re	4215.506	20	Mn	4201.757	40
Zr I	7800.74	2	Fe I	4215.425	60	Ni I	4201.723	30
Sc I	7800.44	40	Na I	4215.4	3	U	4201.628	1
			W	4215.382	12	E r	4201.60	8d
Rb I	7800.227	9000R	Zr I	4215.313	4	Pr	4201.529	30w
			Dy	4215.169	50	Cb	4201.519	10
Si	7800.0	4Wh	Os	4215.155	8	La	4201.50	2
Re	7799.58	3	Pr	4215.14	8	Zr I	4201.457	50
Zr I	7799.51	2	Tb	4215.13	30d	Os	4201.449	30
Ta	7799.51	3	Gd	4215.024	200	U	4201.416	8
Zn I	7799.365	10				Dy	4201.372	8

When prism optics are used, Rb 7800 sometimes suffers intense halation interference from $K \begin{cases} 7664 \\ 7699 \end{cases}$ in potassium-rich minerals (*feldspar* and *mica*).

Rb 4201.851 is liable to CN interference from CN 4216 unless much alkali metal vapor is present and only the early period of arcing is recorded (cf. Ga, Pb, K). When prism optics are employed, direct interference is encountered from Fe 4202.031 in almost all rocks, soils, and many silicate minerals other than *feldspar*. To ascertain whether interference is present and to determine the degree of interference for quantitative analysis, Fe 4143.871 may be used as a check line, as described by Ahrens, 1950, Chap. 12. Because iron is less volatile than rubidium, interference is lowered by recording only the early period of arcing, preferably at a low amperage (3 amp). In basic rocks and mafic minerals, Mn 4201.757 is sometimes emitted.

Rb 4215.556 is rarely usable because of interference from sensitive Sr 4215.524, which is emitted from almost all rocks, soils, and silicate minerals. Rubidium is more volatile than strontium and Rb 4215 can occasionally be used by recording only the early period of arcing and noting the intensity ratio Sr 4215/4077; in the presence of an appreciable trace of rubidium, this ratio is greater than 2.0. The head of CN 4216 is liable to interfere excessively with Rb 4215 if prism optics are used, even if CN emission is comparatively low.

Ruthenium (Ru)

Ionization Potential, 7.5

	Most Sensitive Lines		Excitation Potential	
			Low	High
	3498.942	I (a)	0.0	3.53
	3436.737	I (a)	0.15	3.74

Ce	3499.466	2	Th	3498.625	6
Ce	3499.388	4	U	3498.600	2
Ir I	3499.368	2	Ce	3498.562	8
Tb	3499.34	15	Os	3498.536	80
U	3499.327	6	Cb	3498.434	2
Ce	3499.300	4			
Os	3499.266	3	Ni I	3437.280	600R
Mo	3499.199	3	W II	3437.220	3
Ir I	3499.112	5	Mo	3437.216	25
Er	3499.104	18	Zr II	3437.137	15
Ti I	3499.099	25	Sm II	3437.115	15
Pr	3499.088	40	U	3437.09	3d
Ho	3499.08	10	Ta	3437.074	2r
U	3499.071	6	Fe	3437.051	80
Th	3498.986	8	Th	3437.027	5
Hf	3498.985	6	Ir I	3437.015	20
Ir	3498.951	25	Tb	3436.97	15
Yt I	3498.943	8	Cb	3436.962	20r
			Co I	3436.960	10
Ru I	3498.942	500R	Ce	3436.959	5
Dy	3498.939	15	Dy	3436.95	3
Ce	3498.924	2	Cb	3436.830	2
Mo	3498.923	3	U	3436.780	12
Sc I	3498.912	8			
Ho	3498.87	8	Ru I	3436.737	300R
Ce	3498.826	2	Ce	3436.727	3
Fe	3498.758	1h	Sm	3436.70	3
Ir	3498.737	15	Th	3436.687	3d
Tb	3498.73	8	Pr	3436.629	15
Rh I	3498.730	500	Cu I	3436.543	7
Er	3498.711	10	Yb	3436.46	5
Ce	3498.679	15	Er	3436.336	10
Dy	3498.67	50	Ru I	3436.332	12
Cb	3498.629	30	Ce	3436.304	15

Other sensitive *ruthenium* lines: 3596.179 and 2678.758.

Ionization Potential, 5.6

Most Sensitive Lines			Excitation Potential	
			Low	High
4424.342	II		0.5	3.27
4296.75	I		0.5	3.37
3609.484	II	(b)?	0.3	3.70
3592.595	II	(b)?	0.3	3.81
3568.258	II	(a)?	0.0	3.46

W	4424.906	8	Cb	3610.003	3	Gd	3592.696	50
Ru	4424.781	25	Eu	3609.94	3w	Fe I	3592.692	12
Ir	4424.752	3	Ta	3609.931	1h			
Pr	4424.595	90	Ce	3609.894	2	Sm II	3592.595	40
Er	4424.570	10	Tb	3609.88	8			
V I	4424.563	20	Nd	3609.788	15	Nd	3592.595	20
Ce	4424.540	3	Ir	3609.772	30	V	3592.533	40
Tb	4424.46	3	Co	3609.758	5	Ta	3592.495	2
Ti I	4424.393	15	Ce	3609.687	40	Fe	3592.486	3
Nd	4424.343	50	U	3609.682	15	W II	3592.423	9
			Zr	3609.64	3	Os	3592.317	20
Sm II	4424.342	300	Ti I	3609.591	12	U	3592.301	4
			Tb	3609.55	15	Ho	3592.22	6
Ce	4424.314	6	Pd I	3609.548	1000R	Fe	3592.209	6
Cr I	4424.281	25	Tm	3609.54	15	Ta	3592.14	2
Mo	4424.197	5	Nd	3609.495	25	Dy	3592.117	80
Ce	4424.140	3	Mo	3609.493	5	Nd	3592.073	8
Gd	4424.102	25						
Cr	4424.075	10	Sm II	3609.484	60	Cb	3568.725	5
Rh I	4424.047	5	Cr	3609.479	20	U	3568.690	3
Th	4423.945	8w	Th	3609.447	12	Tm	3568.68	5
Pr	4423.933	5	Er	3609.44	6d	Dy	3568.65	4
V I	4423.914	7	Cb	3609.360	1	Os	3568.566	2
			Ta	3609.357	8	U	3568.525	2
Er	4297.30	2	Ni I	3609.314	200	Ce	3568.513	2
Ca	4297.26	2h	Cu I	3609.307	25	Tb	3568.51	50
Gd	4297.179	100	Ca	3609.30	3	Cb	3568.506	10
U	4297.112	18	V I	3609.289	30w	Ag	3568.435	2
Cr I	4297.050	100	Dy	3609.250	3	Co I	3568.426	2
Ir	4297.030	3	La II	3609.23	2	Fe I	3568.423	20
Ni I	4296.984	2	Th	3609.228	5	Cr	3568.418	6wh
Gd	4296.90	4	Ce	3609.212	2	W	3568.418	4
Sr	4296.82	3	Ta	3609.177	8	Dy	3568.33	4
Ce	4296.786	5	Os	3609.147	20	Pr	3568.29	5
Rh I	4296.770	40	Ru I	3609.107	3			
Er	4296.752	10d	Tb	3609.06	8	Sm II	3568.258	40
			U	3608.96	18	Re	3568.231	40
Sm I	4296.750	100				Mo	3568.181	3
Zr II	4296.742	3				Zr II	3568.135	4
Ru	4296.689	7	Tb	3593.10	15	Ce	3568.126	10
Ce	4296.680	40	Ti II	3593.093	5	Mo	3568.067	3
Cr	4296.631	15	Pr	3593.036	5	W	3568.040	10
Mo	4296.624	15	Ru I	3593.022	60	Sb II	3568.00	1
Fe II	4296.585	2	W	3592.979	5	Ir	3567.995	15
Pr	4296.55	15	Ho	3592.95	6	Cb	3567.995	2
Hf	4296.41	10	Eu	3592.927	7	Th	3567.978	5
Ce	4296.371	10	Yt I	3592.913	80	Tb	3567.86	8
Nd	4296.363	12	Sm	3592.905	4	Lu	3567.84	100
Tb	4296.35	20	Fe I	3592.890	3	Mo	3567.735	2
Dy	4296.34	2	W	3592.846	6d			
Gd	4296.291	40	U	3592.801	1			
Cr	4296.275	15	Th	3592.776	2d			

According to theory, Sm 4296.75 is the most sensitive atom line of samarium. In the arc, however, it does not appear to show very high persistence (cf. Eu, Gd, La, and Y).

Other sensitive *samarium* lines: 3885.284 and 3634.271.

Scandium (Sc)

Ionization Potential, 6.56

Most Sensitive Lines			Excitation Potential	
			Low	High
4246.829	II	(a)	0.3	3.22
4023.688	I	(b)	0.0	3.09
3911.810	I	(b)	0.0	3.18

Fe I	4247.433	200	Pr	4024.07	5	Ce II	3912.189	25
U	4247.430	5	Zr I	4023.981	30	Ta	3912.127	10
Sm II	4247.395	15	Ho	4023.93	4	Ru	3912.112	10
Nd	4247.367	50	Eu	4023.84	2	Fe	3912.05	5wh
Dy	4247.36	30	Ru I	4023.833	25	Cr	3911.999	40wh
U	4247.136	10	Nd	4023.824	12	Pr	3911.989	20d
Eu	4247.069	15	Gd	4023.74	3h	Eu	3911.97	4w
Ce	4246.938	3	Cr	4023.739	40	Mo	3911.945	5
P	4246.88	70	Pr	4023.737	3	Th	3911.914	8
Nd	4246.879	10	Dy	4023.722	10	Er	3911.911	5
			Tb	4023.716	6	Nd	3911.909	12
Sc II	4246.829	80				Cr I	3911.82	10
			Sc I	4023.688	100	Os	3911.812	30
Re	4246.813	25						
Ru	4246.734	20	Ce	4023.640	4	Sc I	3911.810	150
Ce	4246.711	30	U	4023.597	3h			
Tb	4246.59	12	La II	4023.588	50	Ho	3911.80	3
Gd	4246.547	150	Th	4023.533	3	Pr	3911.798	8
Ce	4246.398	10	Cr I	4023.43	15	Re	3911.775	3
Tm	4246.38	20	Co I	4023.403	200	Lu	3911.77	3h
Th	4246.338	3	V II	4023.389	10	Ce	3911.726	3
Ru	4246.334	15	Ce	4023.370	8	Fe	3911.699	1
Cb	4246.295	8	Re I	4023.353	40w	Dy	3911.677	5
U	4246.261	30	Gd I	4023.350	20	U	3911.673	18
			Zr I	4023.302	5	Gd	3911.66	5
			Sc I	4023.223	60	Eu	3911.606	5
Ru	4024.305	7	Sm II	4023.223	30	Er	3911.558	8
Tm	4024.24	7				Mn	3911.419	15
Fe I	4024.104	8	U	3912.234	2	Ti I	3911.362	7
Mo	4024.091	30	Nd	3912.228	20	Th	3911.308	5
Tb	4024.07	40W	V I	3912.207	50	Pr	3911.307	5

Sc 4246.829 is a very satisfactory line for the analysis of the traces of scandium that are so frequently found in most rocks (particularly basic types), soils, and silicate minerals. Fe 4247.433 is emitted from some minerals, rocks, and soils.

According to theory, Sc 5671.80 and Sc 3613.84 are respectively the most sensitive atom and ion lines. In the M.I.T. wavelength tables, Sc 3613 is listed as the most sensitive ion line.

Other sensitive *scandium* lines: 3613.836 and 3630.740.

Ionization Potential, 8.12

Most Sensitive Lines			Excitation Potential	
			Low	High
2881.578	I	(a)?	0.8	5.1
2516.123	I	(a)	0.03	4.9

Th	2882.014	10	W	2516.577	12
Ti I	2881.951	2	Fe I	2516.570	10
Cr	2881.931	1	Yb	2516.362	2
U	2881.909	4	Fe I	2516.250	2
Ce	2881.772	2	Si I	2516.123	500
Ir	2881.737	3			
Ir I	2881.643	7	V	2516.118	25
Dy	2881.59	2h	Re	2516.116	125
Co	2881.580	4	Ta	2516.111	6
			Dy	2516.11	5
Si I	2881.578	500	Mo	2516.109	25
Ce	2881.578	40	Ru	2516.006	20
Gd	2881.578	40	Zn I	2515.807	150w
Ce	2881.420	4s	W II	2515.798	1
Ir	2881.357	4	Ru	2515.759	6
Gd	2881.328	2	Rh I	2515.746	60
Tb	2881.31	10	U	2515.729	6
Ru	2881.276	30	V	2515.723	1
Rh I	2881.254	20	Bi I	2515.686	100
Ta	2881.232	30	Mo	2515.66	10
Cd I	2881.23	50R			
Ir	2881.158	15			
Th	2881.147	10			
Cr	2881.141	25			

Other sensitive *silicon* lines: 3905.528 and 2528.516.

Silver (Ag)

Ionization Potential, 7.54

Most Sensitive Lines			Excitation Potential	
			Low	High
3382.891	I	(a)	0.0	3.65
3280.683	I	(aa)	0.0	3.75

Pr	3383.376	15	U	3281.115	2
Ce	3383.279	8	Ce	3281.095	18
Sb	3383.137	40	Mo	3281.068	25
Th	3383.120	5	Th	3281.034	2
Yt	3383.05	3	Os	3280.915	5
Zr	3382.90	3	Yt II	3280.913	8
Er	3382.892	18	Ta	3280.872	3
Ag	**3382.891**	**1000R**	Sm	3280.842	20
			Mn	3280.756	60
Ce	3382.888	8	Zr II	3280.748	3
Yt	3382.83	3	Th	3280.736	2d
Nd	3382.811	200	Cu	3280.685	10
Tb	3382.80	15	**Ag**	**3280.683**	**2000R**
Ce	3382.698	8			
Cr II	3382.683	35	Co	3280.681	2
U	3382.675	4	Mo	3280.671	3
Pr	3382.660	10	Ce	3280.668	6
W	3382.606	10	U	3280.608	1
Ce	3382.512	8	Rh I	3280.55	30R
Mo	3382.484	15	Lu	3280.50	10
Eu	3382.412	2h	Ce II	3280.485	15
Fe I	3382.409	50	U	3280.399	5
			Ti	3280.391	3
			Th	3280.374	10
			Mo	3280.318	5
			Tb	3280.28	30
			Fe	3280.261	150

Mn 3280.756 is emitted from some basic rocks, mafic minerals and from manganese-rich *sphalerite* and can interfere with Ag 3280 unless a large dispersion is used.

Ionization Potential, 5.12

	Most Sensitive Lines			Excitation Potential Low	High
	5895.923	I	(a)	0.0	2.09
	5889.953	I	(aa)	0.0	2.10
	3302.988	I	(b)	0.0	3.74
	3302.323	I	(bb)	0.0	3.74

Yb	5896.61	5	W	3303.335	7	Yb	3302.44	7
Sm	5896.278	5	Cb	3303.320	1	Ta	3302.328	3
Na I	5895.923	5000R	Mn	3303.278	40	Na I	3302.323	600R
			Ce II	3303.225	10			
Pb	5895.70	20hl	Re	3303.212	30	U	3302.26	1h
Tm	5895.626	80	Mo	3303.113	4	Re	3302.227	30
Nd	5895.578	2	La II	3303.11	400	Cr	3302.19	50h
Fe	5895.497	4	Ir I	3303.091	3	Cb	3302.176	5
Eu	5895.288	25	Na I	3302.988	300R	Yt	3302.17	5
						Pd I	3302.128	100wh
			Zn	3302.941	700R	Pt	3302.12	2h
Co I	5890.484	7	Ca	3302.94	4	Ti II	3302.096	8
Hf	5890.45	8	Ce	3302.913	10W	Sm	3302.092	8
W	5890.333	7	Cr	3302.876	30	Dy	3302.02	2
Cr	5889.989	12	Fe II	3302.859	1	Eu	3301.95	25
Mo	5889.978	50h	U	3302.82	6	Er	3301.93	15
Na I	5889.953	9000R	Ta	3302.765	50	Ru	3301.911	30
			Zr II	3302.666	10	Ce	3301.905	10
Sm	5889.695	20	Pr	3302.66	15	Pr	3301.898	10
Tb	5889.06	10	Tb	3302.64	8	Ta	3301.895	25
			Cb	3302.621	1	Pt I	3301.861	300
			Zn I	3302.588	800	W II	3301.85	1
Th	3303.487	5	Bi	3302.55	150	Ir I	3301.757	2
Fe II	3303.471	5	U	3302.492	3	U	3301.754	10
U	3303.370	4	Dy	3302.472	4	Sr I	3301.734	100
Mo	3303.342	25	Tm	3302.45	125			

Interference from Zn 3302.941 with Na 3302.988 is rare in most rocks, soils, and silicate minerals, and radiation at λ 3302 is invariably due to sodium. In *biotite,* however, appreciable emission may be due to zinc. If present, Zn 3302.588 is usually resolved from Na 3302.988 and Na. 3302.323.

Other sensitive *sodium* lines: 5688.22 and 5682.657.

Strontium (Sr)

Ionization Potential, 5.67

Most Sensitive Lines			Excitation Potential	
			Low	High
4607.331	I	(a)	0.0	2.68
4077.714	II	(a)	0.0	3.03

Tb	4607.81	4	V I	4077.977	2
Fe I	4607.654	50	Dy	4077.974	150r
Mn	4607.625	50	Tb ·	4077.97	25
Nd	4607.381	25	Er	4077.970	20s
Au I	4607.34	30	Hg I	4077.811	150
Sr I	4607.331	1000R	U	4077.786	15
			Ta	4077.721	4
Co	4607.33	2h	Sn	4077.72	2
bh La	4607.3	3	Cu	4077.716	5
Ce	4607.290	3	Sr II	4077.714	400r
V	4607.226	4			
Ce	4607.087	2	Pr	4077.69	4
Mo	4607.075	8	Mo	4077.682	8
Pr	4606.920	3	Cr	4077.677	30
Ru	4606.833	4	Nd	4077.620	8
			Rh I	4077.57	5
Eu	4078.231	3	Ce II	4077.470	18
Pr	4078.16	5	Co I	4077.406	100wh
W	4078.124	7	Yt I	4077.366	50
Re	4078.124	10	Dy	4077.35	4
Mo	4078.074	4	La II	4077.340	600
Ho	4078.00	3	Yb	4077.27	30
Pr	4077.98	10	Ti I	4077.153	18

In basic rocks and mafic minerals, Sr 4607.331 must be used with some caution because of possible interference from Fe 4607.654 and Mn 4607.625. Sr 4607 is, however, very sensitive, and in almost all rocks, soils, and silicate minerals, radiation at λ 4607 is dominantly due to strontium. In lithium minerals, halation interference from Li 4603 may be excessive.

CN emission must be kept at a minimum when Sr 4077 is used.

Other sensitive *strontium* lines: 4832.075 and 4215.524.

Ionization Potential, 6

Most Sensitive Lines   Excitation Potential

3311.162
2714.674   (a)

Sc II	3311.708	3		Fe	2715.125	5
Dy	3311.51	5		Th	2715.092	6
Ce	3311.497	15		Rh I	2715.045	50
Fe I	3311.453	1		V	2715.031	10
Ce	3311.388	3		U	2714.998	6
W	3311.382	15ℓ		Ce	2714.975	5
U	3311.35	4d		Fe I	2714.868	40
Zr II	3311.339	8		W	2714.815	4
Cb	3311.338	5		Ce	2714.723	5
Cr I	3311.30	8		**Ta**	**2714.674**	**200**
Ta	**3311.162**	**300w**		Os	2714.642	50r
W	3311.112	5		Th	2714.617	2h
Er	3311.09	3		U	2714.584	10
Pd	3311.023	4		Ir I	2714.550	4
Ir I	3311.023	2		La I	2714.538	6
Cu I	3311.00	3		Co II	2714.418	12
Dy	3310.96	5		Fe II	2714.412	200
Ru I	3310.957	30		Rh I	2714.410	150
Os	3310.912	200		U	2714.291	2
Nd	3310.900	25		Zr II	2714.258	7
Ce	3310.877	10		V	2714.199	60
U	3310.87	2d				
Hf II	3310.856	15				
Eu	3310.80	3wh				
Tb	3310.80	8				
Mo	3310.771	20				
Sm II	3310.655	25				

Other sensitive *tantalum* lines: 3318.84 and 2647.472.

Tellurium (Te)

Ionization Potential, 9.01

	Most Sensitive Lines	Excitation Potential	
		Low	High
	2385.76 I	0.6	5.8
	2383.25 I	0.6	5.8
	2142.75 I (a)	0.0	5.8

Cr I	2386.19	20	Ir	2383.789	15	Os	2143.23	12
W	2386.17	8	Ta	2383.72	6	Cb	2143.21	4
Ir	2386.153	15	Tm	2383.67	15	V II	2143.047	10
Rh	2386.14	80	Pt I	2383.641	30	Re	2143.00	10
Os	2386.04	2	Sb	2383.63	75	Cb	2142.91	1h
Fe I	2385.95	4	W	2383.54	2h	Ir	2142.82	3
Ir	2385.863	20	Mo	2383.52	12	La	2142.81	2h
Co	2385.816	9	Re	2383.48	25	Re	2142.78	10
Te I	2385.76	600	Co II	2383.46	15	Te I	2142.75	600
			Ir	2383.450	2			
Cr I	2385.74	25	V	2383.436	2	Os	2142.73	4
Ta	2385.73	8	Rh	2383.40	50	Pd	2142.57	3
Fe	2385.579	2	Cr I	2383.33	20	Ta	2142.53	8h
U	2385.55	3				W	2142.511	3
Re	2385.50	12	Te I	2383.25	500	Pt II	2142.499	2
W II	2385.49	3	Fe II	2383.241	8	Os	2142.38	4
Os	2385.49	15	Os	2383.21	15	Rh	2142.28	3
Rh	2385.44	3	Ir	2383.168	10	Ir	2142.25	20
Ta	2385.35	2	Fe II	2383.055	6			
U	2385.28	2	V	2383.001	8			
			W	2382.986	15			
			Rh	2382.89	50			
			Dy	2382.85	2			
			Pd II	2382.756	2			

Te 2142 is at a wavelength where the sensitivity of most photographic emulsions decreases rapidly (cf. the use of Zn 2138).

In some telluride ores, Fe 2383.24 interferes with Te 2383.25. Use may be made of the greater volatility of tellurium to reduce such interference (Ahrens and Liebenberg, 1946).

Ionization Potential, 6.7

Most Sensitive Lines   Excitation Potential

4326.48
4278.51
3676.35
3509.17   (a)?

Ti I	4326.967	12	W	4278.410	10	W	3509.669	8
U	4326.927	3	Th	4278.323	8	U	3509.668	10
Ce	4326.826	15	Ce	4278.248	10	Ce	3509.531	3
Ru I	4326.825	20	Ti I	4278.227	50	Sm	3509.447	4
Fe I	4326.760	10	Gd	4278.202	6	Dy	3509.41	6
Mn	4326.756	80	U	4278.171	5	Ho	3509.35	6
Mo	4326.743	50	Pr	4278.04	35	U	3509.349	3
U	4326.595	2				Zr I	3509.323	40
Tb	**4326.48**	**150**	Sm	3676.837	10	Ce	3509.313	3
			W	3676.802	10	Ce II	3509.254	10
Sr I	4326.445	8	Th	3676.694	6	Ir I	3509.241	8
Eu	4326.44	8w	V I	3676.684	300	Nd	3509.235	10d
U	4326.426	2	Ru	3676.670	8	Ru	3509.201	10
Yb	4326.40	20h	Ir	3676.656	15			
Ho	4326.39	2	Eu	3676.62	20w	**Tb**	**3509.17**	**200**
Dy	4326.39	2	Sc	3676.604	2			
Ti I	4326.355	60	Ho	3676.59	6	Fe I	3509.132	2
Cb	4326.327	30	Re	3676.572	8	U	3509.122	1
Gd	4326.291	3	Dy	3676.56	6	Sm	3509.117	8
Os	4326.254	30	U	3676.560	3	Th	3509.113	4
Hf	4326.24	6h	Co	3676.554	100	Ce	3509.061	2
La I	4326.185	5	Er	3676.508	20	V	3509.041	2
Mo	4326.137	50	Ca bh	3676.5	8	W	3509.015	9
Eu	4326.13	4w	Ru	3676.408	5	Dy	3509.00	6
Sm	4326.127	2	**Tb**	**3676.35**	**100**	Er	3508.938	5
U	4325.897	10				Ce	3508.865	2
			Cr	3676.322	40	Eu	3508.859	10
			Sm	3676.315	8	Os	3508.851	8
Pr	4278.99	15	Fe I	3676.314	200	U	3508.846	8
W	4278.93	4	Cb	3676.312	10	Cr	3508.836	12h
V	4278.883	2	W	3676.311	6	Er	3508.811	8
Ce II	4278.866	20	Mo	3676.235	8	Eu	3508.740	8
Ti I	4278.813	25	Ce	3676.156	12	W	3508.735	9
Ru	4278.689	7	Eu	3676.14	2w	Ir I	3508.719	2
Mn	4278.676	15	Zr	3676.030	2h	Ce	3508.711	12
Pr	4278.62	10	Dy	3676.01	6			
Dy	4278.61	3	Re	3676.002	20			
Rh I	4278.598	25	Mo	3675.981	10			
Mo	4278.584	5	Pr	3675.915	6			
Tb	**4278.51**	**200**	Er	3675.85	2W			
			Tb	3675.78	30			

Other sensitive *terbium* lines: 3585.03, 3561.74 and 3324.40.

Thallium (Tl)

Ionization Potential, 6.07

Most Sensitive Lines			Excitation Potential	
			Low	High
5350.46	I	(aa)	1.0	3.27
3775.72	I	(a)	0.0	3.27
3519.24	I	(b)	1.0	4.47

Ti I	5351.084	50	U	3775.991	10	Ni I	3519.766	500h
Cb	5351.045	3	Ce	3775.986	12	Tb	3519.76	50
Zr I	5350.899	2	Th	3775.942	20	Ce	2519.736	18
Cb	5350.742	150	Fe I	3775.868	2	Th	3519.693	3d
Sm	5350.618	15	Ca	3775.86	2	Cb	3519.649	5
			Sm	3775.849	2	Ru	3519.635	70
Tl I	5350.46	5000R	Bi	3775.745	2	Zr I	3519.605	100
			Tl I	3775.72	3000	Rh I	3519.541	40
W	5350.445	18				Cr	3519.45	6h
Er	5350.44	12	V I	3775.719	30	Cb	3519.334	2
Gd	5350.406	25	Rh I	3775.716	8			
Eu	5350.399	60h	Eu	3775.69	4W	Tl I	3519.24	2000R
Re	5350.392	2w	Er	3775.665	8			
Zr II	5350.353	4	Mo	3775.647	15	Bi	3519.18	10
Sc I	5350.296	3	U	3775.608	12	Os	3519.176	15
Zr II	5350.093	4	Ni I	3775.572	500h	V I	3519.167	10
U	5349.917	5	Ce	3775.564	4	Pr	3519.128	10
			Nd	3775.501	10	Er	3519.094	20rh
			Re	3775.464	10	Ce	3519.077	25
V I	3776.157	50	Zr I	3775.461	7	Ru	3518.983	30
Ce	3776.146	5	Sm	3775.459	10	Tb	3518.96	15
Mo	3776.104	5	Cb	3775.448	5	U	3518.951	3
Pr	3776.089	8	W	3775.446	8	Os	3518.942	20
Sm	3776.06	15	U	3775.442	4	Ir I	3518.906	2h
Ti II	3776.059	8	Eu	3775.41	4W	Eu	3518.904	5
Tb	3776.02	8	Ce	3775.363	2	Th	3518.894	3d
Dy	3776.01	2	Th	3775.319	20	Fe I	3518.882	10
Ba	3776.0	3	U	3775.262	6	Zr	3518.869	4
						Hf II	3518.752	5

Ca 5349.474 (not listed above) in particular, and less often Ti 5351.084, are emitted from many rocks, soils, and silicate minerals and may interfere with Tl 5350.46 if prism optics are used. Occasionally interference from components of CaF 5291 is present in the spectra of phosphate-rich soils.

For Tl 3775, emission from CN 3883 must be effectively quenched, otherwise CN interference is excessive. As thallium is volatile, use may be made of alkali metal vapors for this purpose (cf. Ga, Pb, and Rb), as has been done by Ahrens (1945). This should enable the analyst to detect thallium in *mica*, *potash feldspar*, and some potash-rich rocks. In basic rocks and some mafic minerals, there is some detectable emission from Ni 3775.572; in these rocks and minerals, however, thallium is rarely sought because it is at a concentration well below detection limits. In sulfide minerals, Tl 3775 is sometimes emitted, and in some there is interfering emission by Ni 3775.

Ionization Potential,

	Excitation Potential	
Most Sensitive Lines	Low	High
4019.137 II (a)?	0.0	3.07
2837.299		

Pb	4019.639	6		Re	2837.549	40
Ru I	4019.553	12		Nd	2837.51	5
Dy	4019.48	5		Os	2837.422	25
Ce	4019.480	6		W	2837.344	12
Pr	4019.44	10		U	2837.328	10
Co I	4019.302	80		Ir I	2837.327	20
Ce II	4019.280	4		Mo	2837.320	5h
W	4019.231	18				
U	4019.203	6		Th	2837.299	15
Ce	4019.193	2		Sc	2837.293	4h
Co I	4019.140	5		Ce	2837.289	50s
				Ru	2837.274	20
Th II	4019.137	8		Zr I	2837.232	100
Re I	4019.130	15		Pt I	2837.230	2
Tb	4019.12	40		U	2837.187	10
Ni I	4019.046	5		Co I	2837.151	75r
Mo	4019.046	2		Er	2837.106	5
Ce	4019.044	15		Nd	2837.10	5
U	4018.990	25		Fe	2837.03	1
Ce	4018.919	2		Re	2837.015	2h
Nd	4018.826	15		Dy	2836.994	2h
Sm II	4018.539	4		Mo	2836.965	8
				Gd	2836.955	2
				In I	2836.919	80
W	2837.762	10		U	2836.918	5
U	2837.726	6		Cd I	2836.907	200
Dy	2837.613	2		Mo I	2836.705	1
Ce	2837.598	8		V I	2836.698	10

Thulium (Tm)*

Ionization Potential,

Most Sensitive Lines		Excitation Potential	
		Low	High
3761.917	II		
3761.333	II		
3717.92	I (a)?	0.0	3.28
3462.20	II	0.0	3.28

Pr	3762.366	5	Pr	3761.381	8	Pr	3717.841	8
Th	3762.363	10	Ta	3761.349	8	Th	3717.832	20
Nd	3762.361	10	Tm II	3761.333	250	Hf	3717.800	20
Tb	3762.34	3	Ti II	3761.323	100	Ce	3717.767	3
Eu	3762.33	9w	Ce	3761.185	3	U	3717.729	6
Ti	3762.305	10	Sm	3761.144	6	Eu	3717.69	18w
Dy	3762.28	3	Eu II	3761.134	10	Ru	3717.682	6
Ce	3762.280	4	Cb	3761.126	15	Cb	3717.542	10
Ce	3762.220	3	Tb	3761.12	15	Gd	3717.487	100w
Gd	3762.212	10	Th	3761.104	15	Ce	3717.484	8
Fe I	3762.209	7	U	3761.044	4	Nd	3717.482	2
Ir	3762.208	2	Re	3761.025	2h	Tb	3717.47	8
U	3762.114	10	Yb	3761.00	3			
Mo	3762.086	10	Pr	3760.956	5	Hf II	3462.641	15
Sr	3762.00	1	Nd	3760.942	10d	Ca	3462.62	2
U	3761.961	2	Gd	3760.931	10	Er	3462.58	10
Ce	3761.953	2	Mo	3760.885	6	Tb	3462.51	8
Ir	3761.941	2	U	3760.884	10	Na II	3462.494	2
Tm II	3761.917	200				Ce	3462.433	8
						Fe I	3462.361	10
Ti II	3761.888	12				Pr	3462.36	3
Cr	3761.868	5h	Fe I	3718.408	80	La	3462.32	2
Pr	3761.867	150	Ru	3718.400	8	Ce	3462.234	3
Mo	3761.755	6	Ce	3718.380	15	Eu	3462.21	5
Ca I	3761.72	2	Os	3718.339	30			
Cr	3761.701	4	Ir	3718.211	3	Tm II	3462.20	250
W	3761.621	7	Ce I,II	3718.190	15	Os	3462.191	20
Pr	3761.606	10	Th	3718.167	15	Sc I	3462.183	4
U	3761.601	2	V II	3718.160	5	Pr	3462.10	6
Nd	3761.575	20	Yt I	3718.108	12	Ru	3462.040	5
Ir I	3761.555	5	U	3718.106	8	Rh I	3462.040	1000
Ru	3761.508	12	Ta	3718.072	2	Ho	3461.96	20
Th	3761.475	10	Pr	3718.016	3h	Gd	3461.956	5
Ce	3761.450	2	La II	3717.98	3	Ru	3461.924	30
V I	3761.442	40	Os	3717.926	10	Pr	3461.873	6
Fe I	3761.408	20	Tm I	3717.92	100	W	3461.814	9
Dy	3761.40	2h						

*See list of sensitive rare earth lines at end of tables.

Other sensitive *thulium* lines: 3848.018 and 3425.08.

Ionization Potential, 7.33

			Excitation Potential	
Most Sensitive Lines			Low	High
3262.328	I	(b)	1.1	4.85
3175.019	I	(a)?	0.4	4.31
2839.989	I	(b)	0.4	4.80

Ir I	3262.930	4	Fe	3262.013	30	Mn	3174.651	15h
Er	3262.80	15	Ir I	3262.010	20	Re I	3174.619	30
Re I	3262.765	25	Ba I	3261.96	40	V	3174.539	1
Os	3262.751	100	Cb	3261.879	10			
Ir I	3262.718	3	Mo	3261.84	2	Fe I	2840.423	125
Tb	3262.68	8				Ta	2840.39	2
Th	3262.671	12				Re I	2840.348	40
Mo	3262.628	15	Fe I	3175.447	200	Gd	2840.236	50
Eu	3262.61	15	U	3175.358	8	W	2840.220	9
Sm	3262.579	3	Ru	3175.298	30	Ir I	2840.219	15
Eu	3262.495	5	Ru	3175.147	20	Ce	2840.156	3
Hf	3262.474	10	Te I	3175.11	30	Th	2840.156	8
Co	3262.435	2	Ce	3175.059	10	V	2840.106	2
Tb	3262.40	2	Mo	3175.049	2	W	2840.097	9
Pr	3262.39	2	Fe	3175.035	1	Cr	2840.021	25
Nd	3262.36	10d				Mn	2840.001	20
Mo	3262.353	8	Sn I	3175.019	500h			
Pb	3262.353	20h				Sn I	2839.989	300R
Sn I	3262.328	400h	Fe	3174.96	5	U	2839.890	18
			Co I	3174.905	80	Tm	2839.85	5
Os I	3262.290	500R	Dy	3174.883	12	W II	2839.810	1
Fe	3262.280	50	La II	3174.88	3	Cb	2839.80	2
Ba I	3262.275	3	Ho	3174.86	6	Ta	2839.778	8
Dy	3262.27	2	U	3174.843	6	U	2839.651	5
Sm II	3262.263	10	Pt I	3174.824	2	Mo	2839.585	25
Mo	3262.188	1	Re	3174.780	20w	Ce	2839.561	5
Ce	3262.138	5	Yb	3174.76	2	Na II	2839.555	2
V I	3262.062	10	Mo	3174.672	4	Fe II	2839.529	4
Dy	3262.02	2	Tb	3174.66	15			

Other sensitive *tin* lines: 3034.12, 3009.14 and 2863.327.

Titanium (Ti)

Ionization Potential, 6.81

	Most Sensitive Lines		Excitation Potential	
			Low	High
	4981.733	I	0.85	3.32
	3653.496	I	0.05	3.43
	3361.213	II (a)?	0.03	3.73
	3349.875	II (a)?	0.05	3.73
	3341.875	I,II	0(I), 0.6(II)	3.69(I), 4.26(II)

Fe	4982.507	200	U	3361.727	15	Ce	3349.405	4
Yt II	4982.142	8	Er	3361.67	6	Au	3349.40	15
Ce	4982.132	8	Ta	3361.640	125W	Cb	3349.348	5
Pr	4981.996	2	Eu	3361.615	2h	W	3349.340	2
Dy	4981.96	2h	Co I	3361.558	80	Th	3349.340	5
Ir	4981.879	3	Ni I	3361.556	500W	Cr	3349.322	35
Mo	4981.827	10	Ce II	3361.555	10	Cu I	3349.292	70
			Sm	3361.435	10	Co I	3349.222	3h
Ti I	4981.733	300	Mo	3361.373	30	Sc I	3349.22	4
			Sc II	3361.270	25	Mo	3349.193	6
Sm II	4981.714	50	Co I	3361.267	18	Hf II	3349.17	5
Re I	4981.714	15	Ti I	3361.263	80r	Cr	3349.072	125
Nd	4981.283	10	Ni I	3361.241	10	Cb	3349.059	80
Th	4980.953	8	Tb	3361.24	3	U	3349.036	4
			Ce	3361.232	8	Ti II	3349.035	125
Au	3653.93	5	Eu	3361.214	20	Th	3348.961	4
Sr I	3653.928	15						
Cr I	3653.912	100	Ti II	3361.213	100	Ce	3342.312	3
Mo	3653.897	3				Fe	3342.292	20
Tb	3653.87	15	U	3361.213	2	V	3342.28	5
Ta	3653.828	3	Au	3361.21	3	Re I	3342.263	200
Fe I	3653.763	25	Bi	3361.209	3	La I	3342.224	80
Ir I	3653.759	2h	Os	3361.149	80	Fe I	3342.216	40
Os	3653.725	30	Ru	3361.148	30	Ce	3342.195	3
Ce	3653.670	18	Re I	3361.142	25	Ti I	3342.151	12
Pr	3653.653	4	W II	3361.107	10	Er	3342.11	7
Re I	3653.615	15	Co I	3361.093	5	Cr	3342.021	6
Cb	3653.615	10	Tm	3361.04	10	Cb	3341.974	100r
Tm	3653.61	30	Er	3361.02	12	Co I	3341.947	25
Yt	3653.606	5	Ce	3360.993	3	Os	3341.914	10
Th	3653.59	3	Ti I	3360.990	10	Fe	3341.905	100
Mo	3653.55	4d	Fe I	3360.928	7	Eu	3341.892	5
W	3653.524	5	Cb	3360.902	3	Dy	3341.88	30
			Pr	3360.900	8			
Ti I	3653.496	500	Rh I	3360.803	2	Ti I,II	3341.875	100
			Ru	3360.792	4			
Au II	3653.491	3	W	3360.741	4	Ce I,II	3341.868	40
Sm	3653.479	15	Gd	3360.716	25	Mo	3341.846	8
Ta	3653.393	3	Ce	3360.714	5	Er	3341.836	18
W	3653.338	1				Sm	3341.832	5
Ir I	3653.323	3	Re I	3349.910	20	Ru	3341.664	70
Sr I	3653.270	30	Sm	3349.835	3	U	3341.664	12
U	3653.209	10	La I	3349.834	4	Ce	3341.640	2
Os	3653.201	10W	Fe	3349.738	1	Er	3341.61	12
Ir	3653.191	15	W	3349.538	4	Cb	3341.600	3
Re	3653.161	4h	Co	3349.526	7	Ti I	3341.554	2
Nd	3653.150	10	Cb	3349.523	30	Hg I	3341.478	100
Sm	3653.113	10	U	3349.43	4d	Pr	3341.473	10
Ce	3653.108	15	Tb	3349.42	30	Sm II	3341.435	5
Tb	3652.97	15				Dy	3341.433	10
			Ti II	3349.406	100			

Ionization Potential, 4

Most Sensitive Lines   Excitation Potential

4244.372
4241.669

Nd	4244.971	10		Ce	4242.009	10
Ce	4244.916	6		Hf II	4241.93	2
Tb	4244.86	2		Co I	4241.886	3h
Ru I	4244.832	25		Dy	4241.83	2
Mo	4244.800	4		Re I	4241.822	2
Dy	4244.79	5		Au I	4241.77	40
Eu	4244.751	10d		Ce	4241.743	3
Sm II	4244.696	100		Pd I	4241.7	2h
Ir	4244.664	2		Zr I	4241.687	100
Nd	4244.562	12				
Ce	4244.552	5		U	4241.669	40
Tb	4244.53	5				
Pr	4244.490	4		Ce	4241.644	2
Ce	4244.470	3		Na I	4241.6	3
Rh I	4244.443	15		Os	4241.521	9
W	4244.373	40		Co I	4241.514	3h
				Cb	4241.449	3
U	4244.372	25		W	4241.448	30
Sm	4244.244	3		Ce II	4241.405	5
Re I	4244.143	30		Re I	4241.387	30
Ta	4243.986	5		V I	4241.318	15
Th	4243.929	12		Pr	4241.30	10
Gd	4243.845	60		Gd	4241.282	10
				Ce	4241.244	3
Tm	4242.15	500		Nd	4241.208	12
Zr I	4242.013	4		Zr I	4241.202	100

According to Strasheim (1950) an iron line (not listed in the M.I.T. tables) interferes with U 4241.669 at relatively low concentrations of iron. In *zircon* and heavy mineral residue fractions (as from beach sand for example), Zr 4241.687 interferes with U 4241.669.

If a relatively small dispersion is used, U 2882.741, 2882.929, and 2882.587 appear as a single line which shows a high sensitivity. For bibliography on the sensitive lines of uranium, see Ahrens, 1950, Chap. 17.

Other sensitive *uranium* lines: 4543.632, 4090.135 and 2882.741.

Vanadium (V)

Ionization Potential, 6.76

Most Sensitive Lines			Excitation Potential	
			Low	High
4379.238	I	(a)	0.3	3.12
3185.396	I	(b)	0.1	3.94

Zr II	4379.776	10	Sm	3185.837	3
bh La	4379.7	20	Mo	3185.711	8
U	4379.644	2	U	3185.71	12
bh La	4379.6	10	Rh I	3185.593	100
Tb	4379.60	3w	Re I	3185.563	200
Pd I	4379.561	6	Eu	3185.56	10wh
Cb	4379.525	2	Ce	3185.506	2
Gd	4379.52	2	Tm	3185.48	20
Dy	4379.41	2	Ru I	3185.442	12
Bi II	4379.4	25	Ce	3185.413	4
Pr	4379.335	100w	U	3185.397	4
Yt I	4379.324	4	V I	3185.396	500R
Tb	4379.26	4			
Ag	4379.25	5	Os	3185.327	150
V I	4379.238	200R	Er	3185.247	15
			W	3185.202	6
Hf	4379.167	10h	U	3185.145	4
Ho	4379.15	3	Mo	3185.104	20
Nd	4379.111	2	Zr I	3185.075	2
Ce	4379.081	3	W II	3185.05	1
Pr	4378.836	3	Th	3184.898	10
Ta	4378.822	40	Ru I	3184.897	4
Ce	4378.818	4	Fe I	3184.896	200
Tb	4378.70	9w	Dy	3184.777	18

Other sensitive *vanadium* lines: 4384.722, 3183.982 and 3093.108.

Ionization Potential, 7.98

	Most Sensitive Lines			Excitation Potential	
				Low	High
	4302.108	I	(a)	0.4	3.23
	4294.614	I	(a)	0.4	3.24
	4008.753	I	(a)	0.4	3.44

Ce	4302.653	10	Th	4295.088	4	Pr	4009.24	5
Dy	4302.57	2	Er	4295.039	15	Gd	4009.21	50
U	4302.530	2	Dy	4295.038	20	Tb	4009.193	5
Ca I	4302.527	50	Ho	4295.01	3	U	4009.170	8
Yt I	4302.294	30	W	4295.005	5	Er	4009.165	15
Fe I	4302.192	50	Dy	4294.936	25	Th	4009.066	10
V I	4302.149	8	Zr I	4294.792	40	Ce	4009.063	121
Bi II	4302.136	2h	Ru I	4294.791	20	Ir I	4008.967	5
			Hf	4294.787	25	Ti I	4008.928	80
W I	4302.108	60	Sc II	4294.767	20	Gd	4008.922	20
Pr	4302.10	60	Ce II	4294.756	10	U	4008.918	8
U	4302.089	5	Nd	4294.735	15	Fe	4008.873	5
Ti II	4301.934	25	Pr	4294.700	25	Eu	4008.872	8w
Mo	4301.932	10	Eu	4294.67	4	Nd	4008.754	12
U	4301.723	6	U	4294.651	3h			
Ho	4301.62	3				W I	4008.753	45
Er	4301.604	25	W I	4294.614	50	Pr	4008.714	150
			Mo	4294.599	6	U	4008.70	2
			Tb	4294.36	10	Ce	4008.664	8
			Fe I	4294.128	700	Dy	4008.49	5
			Ti II	4294.124	60	Hf II	4008.46	5

Fe 4294.128 is intense and may interfere excessively with W 4294.614 in most rocks, soils, and silicate minerals if prism optics are used. In *cassiterite*, a common host mineral for wolfram, W 4294 may be free from interference. Ti 4294.124 is emitted from some rocks, minerals, and soils.

The above comments apply also to W 4008.753 and Ti 4008.928, and W 4302.108 and Fe 4302.192.

Other sensitive *wolfram* lines: 2944.395 and 2946.981.

Ytterbium (Yb)*

Ionization Potential, 6.2

Most Sensitive Lines				Excitation Potential	
				Low	High
3987.994	I	(b)?		0.0	3.09
3694.203	II	(a)		0.0	3.34
3289.37	II	(b)?		0.0	3.75

La II	3988.518	1000	Pr	3694.695	40	Yb	3289.85	1000
Ce	3988.518	8h	Cb	3694.666	10	Yt	3298.85	15
U	3988.293	2	V I	3694.622	60	Mo	3289.844	10
Eu	3988.253	10w	Ag	3694.62	2h	Ta	3289.838	25
Dy	3988.21	4	Ta	3694.519	7h	Ce	3289.790	2
Os	3988.179	50	W	3694.508	10	U	3289.749	2
Cb	3988.157	5	Ir	3694.454	2	Hf II	3289.74	5
U	3988.029	8	Ti I	3694.447	80	Rh	3289.636	50r
Pr	3988.019	25	Dy	3694.36	6	Ce	3289.523	2
Th	3988.015	50	Th	3694.355	5	Cb	3289.450	2
W	3988.007	7	U	3694.325	6	Fe	3289.436	10
			Pr	3694.321	3	V II	3289.389	10
Yb I	3987.994	1000R	Sm	3694.314	15	Eu	3289.38	2
Ce	3987.990	5	La II	3694.27	4	Ho	3289.38	10
Ho	3987.98	8	Ho	3694.24	10			
Er	3987.951	100r						
Re	3987.929	3	Yb II	3694.203	500R	Yb II	3289.37	500R
Cr	3987.89	3	Yt	3694.20	4			
Gd	3987.842	50	Er	3694.193	25d	Er	3289.36	25
Eu	3987.83	20w	Ce	3694.173	4w	Dy	3289.34	2
Ir	3987.829	12	Tb	3694.12	8	U	3289.307	4
Nd	3987.810	25	Mn	3694.115	5	Ce	3289.280	10
Tb	3987.804	4	Gd	3694.011	25	Ru	3289.245	5
Ru	3987.795	3	Fe I	3694.010	400	Rh I	3289.138	150
U	3987.720	2	Sm II	3693.996	100	Cs I	3289.13	2
Th	3987.713	10	Th	3693.94	2	Mo	3289.015	40
Ce	3987.699	2ℓ	Ni I	3693.932	50	V	3288.982	10
Tb	3987.671	6	Dy	3693.84	4	Fe	3288.967	30
Er	3987.663	4	Eu	3693.82	25w	Ce	3288.941	2
Ir I	3987.657	4	Cb	3693.765	1	Ti I	3288.897	2
Ti	3987.610	8	Ce I,II	3693.708	8	Os	3288.837	30
Ho	3987.55	3						
W	3987.524	5						

*See list of sensitive rare earth lines at end of tables.

Other sensitive *ytterbium* lines: 5556.476 and 3289.37.

Ionization Potential, 6.5

	Most Sensitive Lines		Excitation Potential	
			Low	High
	4374.935	II		0.3	3.23
	3710.290	II	(a)	0.2	3.51
	3242.280	II		0.2	3.99

Ti	4375.425	10	U	3710.785	4	Zr I	3242.764	2h
Cr	4375.333	25	Ho	3710.75	8	Pd I	3242.703	2000wh
Tb	4375.33	6	Dy	3710.73	4	Ir I	3242.608	3
Dy	4375.33	10	Cr	3710.60	2	Ta	3242.566	7
V I	4375.304	20	La II	3710.59	3	Ce	3242.539	2
Ce	4375.174	12	U	3710.534	3	Cb	3242.531	3
Sc I	4375.170	3	Sb II	3710.519	2	Dy	3242.51	4
Ta	4375.143	15	Cb	3710.448	15	Sm II	3242.482	4
Eu	4375.12	4	Ru	3710.316	4	Nd	3242.455	4
bh Zr	4375.1	8	Yb	3710.31	4	Cb	3242.415	1
Nd	4375.039	30	U	3710.308	8	Ir I	3242.323	8
Mo	4375.014	8	Sm	3710.300	25	Dy	3242.285	4
Gd	4374.986	25	Er	3710.290	15wh	Yt II	3242.280	60
Sm II	4374.975	200	Yt II	3710.290	80	Fe	3242.272	3
Mn	4374.947	150	Eu	3710.29	20w	Th	3242.257	8
Yt II	4374.935	150	W	3710.289	4	Ru	3242.165	80
Er	4374.925	40wh	Ce	3710.253	2	Zr II	3242.163	1
Co I	4374.925	10	Ti I	3710.186	6	Ce II	3242.135	12
Nd	4374.923	20	U	3710.168	1	Ta	3242.048	125
Lu	4374.90	5	Mo	3710.142	20	Sm	3242.031	40
Mo	4374.888	8	Cr	3710.09	4	W	3242.025	10
Tb	4374.83	6	Dy	3710.080	20	U	3241.991	10
Ti II	4374.822	7	Pr	3710.012	6	Ti II	3241.986	60
Rh I	4374.80	1000W	Eu	3710.01	5	Os	3241.982	15
Dy	4374.80	12	Ti I	3709.961	80	Tb	3241.94	8
Th	4374.790	15	Re I	3709.937	40	Be II	3241.835	5
Cb	4374.783	3	Ce	3709.933	25	Cb	3241.818	2
Ce	4374.760	3	U	3709.878	2	Os	3241.796	15
Ca	4374.61	10	Cb	3709.742	2			
Sc II	4374.455	100						

*See list of sensitive rare earth lines at end of tables.

Y 3710.290 frequently suffers excessive interference from CN 3883, but in granitelike rocks this interference is not always excessive and Y 3710 may sometimes be used (Ahrens, 1950, Chap. 16). In basic rocks, mafic minerals, and many soils, Mn 4374.947 interferes excessively with Y 4374.935.

Although Ti 3241.986 is commonly emitted from many rocks, minerals, and soils, it is usually cleanly resolved from Y 3242.280 in spectrographs normally employed for the analysis of these materials.

Theoretically Y 5466.47 is the most sensitive atom line of yttrium, but it does not appear to show high persistence (cf. Eu, Gd, La, and Sm).

Other sensitive *yttrium* lines: 3774.332 and 3600.734.

Zinc (Zn)

Ionization Potential, 9.36

	Most Sensitive Lines	Excitation Potential	
		Low	High
	4810.534 I (b)	4.1	6.63
	3345.020 I (b)	4.1	7.75
	2138.56 I (a)	0.0	5.8

Mo	4811.062	50	Ru	3345.317	60	Ce	3344.552	4w
U	4810.889	6	Eu	3345.311	3	Yt	3344.55	3
Cr	4810.733	30	Ce	3345.230	3	Ru I	3344.532	60
Cb	4810.597	100	Cr	3345.15	15	Ca I	3344.513	100
Zn I	4810.534	400w	Ta	3345.108	3			
			W	3345.089	9			
Nd	4810.509	2	Nd	3345.088	12	Re	2139.15	18
Rh	4810.487	15	Sm	3345.02	1	Co I	2138.971	15
Ce	4810.392	6				Cb	2138.88	2
Dy	4810.241	2	Zn I	3345.020	800	Os	2138.75	3
Tb	4810.203	3r	Ti I	3344.931	8	Os	2138.61	8
Re	4810.104	4	W II	3344.904	3	Fe I	2138.589	8
Ru	4809.699	4	Th	3344.882	8	Ni I	2138.58	10
			U	3344.870	6	Ir	2138.57	15
			Ru	3344.797	5			
Zn I	3345.572	500	Zr II	3344.786	15	Zn I	2138.56	800R
U.	3345.54	12	Ce II	3344.761	50			
Nd	3345.522	10	Pr	3344.758	2	Cb	2138.552	2
Er	3345.46	6	Er	3344.75	8	As	2138.53	2
Be I	3345.451	2	Mo	3344.746	50	Cu I	2138.507	25wh
Ce	3345.436	20	Ti I	3344.630	2	Os	2138.40	3
Dy	3345.37	3	Pr	3344.564	8	V II	2138.16	8
Cr	3345.37	18	U	3344.561	4	W II	2138.15	10
Mn	3345.352	15	La II	3344.560	300	Fe	2138.01	2

Very sensitive Zn 2138 is not in common use because at its wavelength the sensitivity of the usual photographic emulsion decreases sharply (cf. Te 2142).

Other sensitive *zinc* lines: 4722.159 and 3302.588.

Ionization Potential, 6.92

	Most Sensitive Lines	Excitation Potential	
		Low	High
	4687.803 I	0.7	3.36
	3438.230 II (a)	0.1	3.68
	3391.975 II (a)	0.2	3.80

Hf	4688.39	30	U	3438.407	3	Ce	3392.256	3
Eu	4688.23	100	Ru I	3438.368	70	Ti	3392.197	2
Ce	4688.229	2	Er	3438.32	12	Mo	3392.173	15
Mo	4688.220	25	Eu	3438.31	5	Ho	3392.05	6
Ho	4688.20	2	Pr	3438.31	25w	Th	3392.040	10
Gd	4688.136	20	Fe	3438.306	10	Cu I	3392.016	7
Sm	4688.132	4	Hf II	3438.235	25	Fe	3392.014	20
Re	4687.858	15	Ce	3438.235	3	Tb	3392.01	15
Er	4687.835	3				Eu	3391.992	40
Pr	4687.809	50	Zr II	3438.230	250	Dy	3391.99	4
						Er	3391.989	30
Zr I	4687.803	125	W	3438.210	7			
Cb	4687.781	5	Ir I	3438.094	6	Zr II	3391.975	300
W	4687.653	12	Ce	3438.066	15	Nd	3391.948	6
Ce	4687.637	2	Sm II	3438.054	9	Ru	3391.890	50
Pr	4687.233	3	Yt	3437.953	3	Ce	3391.884	3
			Fe	3437.952	15	Mo	3391.851	1
			U	3437.934	6	Sm	3391.841	2
Yb	3438.72	4	V I	3437.873	2	Rh I	3391.73	3d
Co I	3438.713	80W	Ce	3437.813	10	Tb	3391.72	15
U	3438.697	2	V I	3437.773	4	Th	3391.717	1
Os	3438.611	4				Ce	3391.593	10
Tb	3438.57	15				Cb	3391.591	1
Nd	3438.474	6	Ir	3392.475	2	Lu	3391.55	10
Er	3438.473	9	Re	3392.384	3h	Mo	3391.536	4
Hf	3438.432	12	Cb	3392.338	20r	W	3391.531	10
Cb	3438.419	1	Fe I	3392.313	125	Cr II	3391.434	4

Other sensitive *zirconium* lines: 3601.193 and 3496.210.

Wavelength	Intensity	Sensitivity	

1. Cerium (Ce)

Wavelength	Intensity	(M and S)	(S and W)
4186.599 II	80	1	1
4137.646 II	25	3	3
4133.800 II	35	2	2
4040.762 II	70	5	4
4012.388 I, II	60	4	4
3942.151 II	35	-	4
3801.529 II	25	-	5

2. Dysprosium (Dy)

Wavelength	Intensity		
4211.719 I	200	2	5
4186.810 I	100w	3	-
4045.983 I	150	4	-
4000.454 II	400	-	5
3968.395 II	300	5	-
3944.692 II	300	-	4
3645.416	300	-	2
3531.712	100	1	1
3407.80	150	-	3

3. Erbium (Er)

Wavelength	Intensity		
4007.967 I	35	4	3
3906.316 II	25	5	3
3692.652	20	2	2
3499.104	18	3	3
3372.750	35	1	1

4. Europium (Eu)

Wavelength	Intensity		
4205.046 II	200R	2	2
4129.737 II	150R	3	3
3971.99 I	1000R wh	5	5
3930.503 II	1000R	4	4
3819.66 II	500 wd	1	1

5. Gadolinium (Gd)

Wavelength	Intensity		
3768.405	20	4	4
3646.196	200w	5	5
3422.466	80	1	1
3362.244	150	2	2
3350.482	150	3	3

6. Holmium (Ho)

Wavelength	Intensity		
4103.84 I	400	4	3
4053.92 I	400	5	5
3891.02 II	200	2	2
3796.73	20	3	4
3456.00	60	1	1
3398.98	40	-	5

Wavelength	Intensity	Sensitivity	
7. Lanthanum (La)		(M and S)	(S and W)
4086.714 II	500	3	5
3988.518 II	1000	2	2
3949.106 II	1000	1	1
3794.773 II	400	5	4
3790.822 II	400	4	3
8. Lutecium (Lu)			
3507.39 II	100	4	3
3397.07 II	50	-	-
3359.56 I	150	5	4
3077.60 II	100	3	5
2911.39 II	100	2	2
2615.42 II	100	1	1
9. Neodymium (Nd)			
4303.573 II	100	1	5
4156.083 II	10	4	4
4109.455 II	30	5	3
4061.085 II	40	3	2
4012.250 II	80	2	1
10. Praseodymium (Pr)			
4225.327 II	50	4	3
4222.98 II	125	5	5
4179.422 II	200	2	4
4100.746 II	200	3	2
3908.431 II	100	1	1
11. Samarium (Sm)			
3885.284 II	50	5	5
3634.271 II	100	4	3
3609.484 II	60	3	2
3592.595 II	40	2	1
3568.258 II	40	1	4
12. Terbium (Tb)			
3874.18 II	200	-	*
3676.35	100	3	
3585.03	15	2	
3561.74	200	4	
3509.17	200	1	
3324.40	70	5	

*No sample available.

Wavelength	Intensity	Sensitivity	
13. Thulium (Tm)			
3848.018	400	2	
3795.765	250	5	
3717.92	100	1	
3462.20	250	3	
3425.08	200	4	
3362.61	250	-	
14. Ytterbium (Yb)			
7699.49	2000	5	-
5556.476 I	1500	4	-
3987.994 I	1000R	3	3
3694.203 II	500R	1	2
3289.37 II	500R	2	1
15. Yttrium (Y)			
4374.935 II	150	2	5
4102.376 I	150	5	-
3774.332 II	12	3	2
3710.290 II	80	1	1
3600.734 II	100	4	3
3242.280 II	60	-	4

*No sample available

Visual (spectroscopic) sensitivities

Element	λ	Sensitivity (%)
Ag	5465.5, 5209.1	.001 - .01
Al	3961.5, 3944.0	.001 - .01
Au	4792.6	0.5
B (BO)	diffuse BO bands	> 1
Ba	5535.5, 4934.1, 4554.1	.0001 - .001
Be	4572.7	.1 - 1
Bi	4722.5	.001 - .01
Br (BaBr)	5360.1, 5208.2	barely perceptible
Ca	4226.7	.0001
Cd	5085.8, 4799.9, 4678.2	.001 - .01
Ce	5512.1, 4628.2	no standards, perhaps 0.1 - 1
Cl (CaCl)	6211.6, 5934.0	no standards, perhaps 1
Co	4867.9, 4840.3, 4813.5, 4792.9	0.1 - 1
Cr	5208.4, 5206.0, 5204.5	.001 - .01
Cs	4593.2, 4555.4	no standards
Cu	5218.2, 5153.3, 5105.6	.001 - .01
Dy	4957.4	no standards, perhaps .1 - 1
F (CaF)	6064.4, 5291.0	.001 - .01
Fe	5371.5, 5328.5, 5269.5	.1
Ga	4172.1	.001 - .01
Gd	5155.8, 5103.5, 5015.1	no standards, perhaps .1 - 1
Ge	4685.8, 4226.6	? (no standards) ? (Ca interference)
Hf	4093.2	no standards
Hg	5460.7	no standards
In	4511.3	.001
Ir	5449.5	1
K	7699.0, 7664.9, 6939.0, 6911.3	.5
La	4921.8, 4899.9	.1
Li	6707.8	.00001
Mg	5183.6, 5172.7, 5167.3	.001 - .01
Mn	4823.5, 4783.4, 4766.4, 4762.4, 4754.0	.001 - .01
Mo	5570.5, 5533.0, 5506.5	.001 - .01
Na	5895.9, 5889.9	.0001 - .001
Nd	5319.8, 5293.2	no standards, perhaps .1 - 1
Ni	5476.9	.01 - .1
Os	4420.5	.1 - 1
Pb	4057.8	.001 - .01
Pd	5295.6, 5163.8, 4212.9	.01 - .1
Pr	5110.8	no standards
Pt	5059.5	.1 - 1
Rb	6298.3	no standards
Re	5275.5, 4889.2	no standards
Rh	5599.4, 4374.8	.1 - 1
Ru	5171.0, 4554.5	.01 - .1
Sb	4033.5	> 5
Sc	5087.1, 5085.5, 5083.7, 5081.6	.005 - .05
Si	3905.5	1 - 10
Sm	4883.9, 4815.8, 4760.3	no standards, perhaps .1 - 1
Sn	4524.7	.1 - 1
Sr	4607.3, 4215.5, 4077.7	.0001 - .001
Ta	5402.5, 4812.7	.5
Th	6408.6	.5
Tl	5014.3, 5007.0, 4999.5, 4999.1, 4891.7	.001 - .01
Tl	5350.5	.001 - .01
U	5915.4	.5
V	4881.5, 4875.5, 4864.7, 4851.5, 4832.4, 4827.4	.01 - 1
W	5224.7, 5053.3	.1
Y (Y, YO, YO)	5087.4, 6132.1, 5972.2	.001 - .01
Zn	4810.5, 4722.2, 4680.1	.001 - .01
Zr	4815.6, 4772.3, 4739.5, 4710.1, 4687.8	.01

PERIODIC TABLE OF THE ELEMENTS

OUTER ELECTRONS ARE IN THE	I	II	III	IV	V	VI	VII	VIII	O
1st or K shell	1 H 1.0078								2 He 4.003
2nd or L shell	3 Li 6.940	4 Be 9.02	5 B 10.82	6 C 12.00	7 N 14.008	8 O 16.0000	9 F 19.00		10 Ne 20.183
3rd or M shell	11 Na 22.994	12 Mg 24.32	13 Al 26.97	14 Si 28.06	15 P 30.98	16 S 32.06	17 Cl 35.457		18 A 39.944
4th or N shell	19 K 39.096	20 Ca 40.08	21 Sc 45.10	22 Ti 47.90	23 V 50.95	24 Cr 52.01	25 Mn 54.93	26 Fe 55.85 27 Co 58.94 28 Ni 58.69	
	29 Cu 63.57	30 Zn 65.38	31 Ga 69.72	32 Ge 72.60	33 As 74.91	34 Se 78.96	35 Br 79.916		36 Kr 83.7
5th or O shell	37 Rb 85.48	38 Sr 87.63	39 Y 88.92	40 Zr 91.22	41 Nb 92.91	42 Mo 95.95	43 Tc	44 Ru 101.7 45 Rh 102.91 46 Pd 106.7	
	47 Ag 107.880	48 Cd 112.41	49 In 114.76	50 Sn 118.70	51 Sb 121.76	52 Te 127.61	53 I 126.92		54 Xe 131.3
6th or P shell	55 Cs 132.91	56 Ba 137.36	57 La 138.92 [*]	72 Hf 178.6	73 Ta 180.88	74 W 183.92	75 Re 186.31	76 Os 190.2 77 Ir 193.1 78 Pt 195.23	
	79 Au 197.2	80 Hg 200.61	81 Tl 204.39	82 Pb 207.21	83 Bi 209.00	84 Po 210	85 At 212.7		86 Rn 222
7th or R shell	87 Fr 223.7	88 Ra 226.05	89 Ac 227.05	90 Th 232.12	91 Pa 231.?	92 U 238.07	TRANSURANIC ELEMENTS 93 Np 94 Pu 95 Am 96 Cm		

* THE RARE EARTHS	58 Ce 140.13	59 Pr 140.92	60 Nd 144.27	61 Pm 146.0	62 Sm 150.43	63 Eu 152.0	64 Gd 156.9	65 Tb 159.2	66 Dy 162.46	67 Ho 164.94	68 Er 167.20	69 Tm 169.4	70 Yb 173.04	71 Lu 174.99

SOME REVISIONARY DATA ON THE M.I.T.
WAVELENGTH TABLES

1. Coincident rare earth lines.

Smith and Wiggins (1949) have drawn attention to the fact that in the M.I.T. tables, faint lines of rare earth elements frequently coincide with sensitive lines of other rare earths. Some of the rare earth compounds, particularly that of erbium, which were available when the M.I.T. wavelength program was undertaken, evidently contained traces of other rare earths. Line coincidence does, of course, not necessarily mean that in each example the faint line does not exist, but the data indicate that this is so in a high proportion of such examples. As the examples cited by Smith and Wiggins are of some significance, particularly for the analysis of rare earth mixtures, their observations are given here. Gatterer and Junkes (1945) have published charts and tables on rare earth spectra. Several references to other publications on rare earth spectra are given by them.

Smith and Wiggins give some additional information in their paper and point out that their observations should not be regarded as complete.

They also state that no examples of impurity coincidences were observed for La, Lu, Tm, and Yb.

2. Other data (mainly line coincidence).

Sn 4511.30 200, coincident with In 4511.323 5000. In a specimen of pure *cassiterite* (SnO_2), a doubtful haze was all that could be observed at λ 4511 by Ahrens (1948). Apparently Sn 4511 is extremely weak or nonexistent. (See Arnolds (1914) as original source for Sn 4511.) This observation is of some significance because In 4511 is indium's most sensitive line and frequently tin and indium are associated in minerals.

Tl II 3261.605 70, should be Ti II 3261.605. Of some importance, as Ti 3261 is commonly emitted in minerals, rocks, and soils. With a limited dispersion, a line at λ 3261 could be mistaken for Cd 3261.057, Sn 3262.328, or Os 3262.290 (sensitive lines of these elements).

Fe 2852.13 150, coincident with sensitive Mg 2852.129. Fe 2852 is either extremely faint or nonexistent.

Ca 7203.17 200 and Ca 7202.194 30. According to R. Wilds (private communication to G. R. Harrison), Ca 7203.17 should be deleted.

Co 6707.857 200 and Mo 6707.85 300, coincident with Li 6707.844 3000. Co 6707 and Mo 6707 probably nonexistent or extremely faint.

Cu 2592.627 1000. According to H. Gutsche (private communication to G. R. Harrison) this line is probably nonexistent.

Eu 3280.682 1000, with Ag 3280.683 2000. Gatterer and Junkes (1945) do not list this europium line.

Li 6240.1 300. Is extremely faint. Some of the sodium doublets in the yellow-green require investigation. Some of these (5688.2 and 5682.7 excepted) which have listed intensities of a hundred or so either extremely faint or perhaps undetectable.

3. Two lines which should be added.

Fe 4303.585 This is listed (with intensity of "25") in the original cards from which the M.I.T. tables were prepared. It is coincident with Nd 4303.573, the most sensitive line of neodymium, a relatively common rare earth element; for further comments see Ahrens (1950), p. 186.

Fe 4241.7 According to Strasheim (1950) there is emission of an iron line at λ 4241.7 that coincides with U 4241.669, probably the most sensitive line of uranium.

COINCIDENT RARE EARTH LINES IN M.I.T. TABLES

(*after Smith and Wiggins*)

	Faint line			Coincident sensitive line	
		Int.			Int.
Ce	3995.752	6	La II	3995.750	600
	3988.518	8 h	La II	3988.518	1000
	3987.990	5	Yb I	3987.994	1000 R
	3219.948	2	Tb	3219.95	50
Dy	4040.76	6	Ce II	4040.762	70
	3634.27	3	Sm II	3634.271	100
	3494.78	2	Ho	3494.77	30

Coincident rare earth lines (cont.)

Faint line		Int.	Coincident sensitive line		Int.
Er	4086.713	8 s	La II	4086.714	500
	4077.970	20 s	Dy	4077.974	150 r
	4061.082	5	Nd II	4061.085	40
	4031.690	6 w	La II	4031.692	400
	4012.253	12	Nd II	4012.250	80
	4000.452	35	Dy II	4000.454	400
	3941.515	5	Nd	3941.512	60
	3710.290	15 wh	Y II	3710.290	80
	3531.714	40	Dy	3531.712	100
	3494.494	15	Dy	3494.496	100
	3456.003	25 d	Ho	3456.00	60
	3289.36	25	Yb II	3289.37	500 R
Eu	3462.21	5	Tm	3462.20	250
	3289.38	2	Yb II	3289.37	500 R
Ho	4007.96	4	Er I	4007.967	35
	4000.45	5	Dy II	4000.454	400
	3898.55	6	Dy	3898.544	100
	3692.65	10	Er	3692.652	20
	3645.41	8	{ La II	3645.414	100
			} Dy	3645.416	300
	3600.73	6	Y II	3600.734	100
	3289.38	10	Yb II	3289.37	500 R
Nd	3306.375	12	Sm II	3306.372	100
Sm	4133.797	2	Ce II	4133.800	35
	3819.678	10	Eu II	3819.66	500 wd
Tb	4186.60	2	Ce II	4186.599	80
	4077.97	25	Dy	4077.974	150 r
Y	3694.20	4	Yb II	3694.203	500 R
	3372.77	15	Er	3372.750	35

BIBLIOGRAPHY

AHRENS, L. H. (1945b). Geochemical studies on some of the rarer elements in South African minerals and rocks. II. The geochemical relationship between thallium and rubidium in minerals of igneous origin. *Trans. Geol. Soc. S. Afr.*, **48**, 207.

AHRENS, L. H. (1948). Evidence of geological age against decay of Sn^{115} to In^{115} by electron capture. *Nature*, **162**, 413.

AHRENS, L. H. (1950). *Spectrochemical analysis.* Addison-Wesley Press, Cambridge.

AHRENS, L. H. and LIEBENBERG, W. R. (1946). Qualitative spectrochemical analysis of minerals and rocks. *Trans. Geol. Soc. S. Afr.*, **49**, 133.

ARNOLDS, R. (1914). The arc and spark spectrum of tin in I. A. (7800 to 2069). *Zeit. f. wiss. Phot.*, **13**, 313.

DINGLE, H. (1950). *Practical applications of spectrum analysis.* Chapman and Hall, London.

GATTERER, A. and JUNKES, J. (1945). *Spektren der seltenen Erden.* Specola Vaticana, Vatican City.

HARRISON, G. R. (1939). *M. I. T. wavelength tables.* John Wiley and Sons, New York.

MEGGERS, W. F. (1941a). Notes on the physical basis for spectrographic analysis. *J. Op. Soc. Am.*, **31**, 39.

MEGGERS, W. F. (1941b). The strongest lines of singly ionized atoms. *J. Op. Soc. Am.*, **31**, 605.

PEARSE, R. W. B. and GAYDON, A. G. (1950). *The identification of molecular spectra.* John Wiley and Sons, New York.

PREUSS, E. (1938). Quantitative spectral analysis in the carbon arc. *Zeit. angew. Mineral.*, **1**, 168.

SMITH, D. M. and WIGGINS, G. M. (1949). Analysis of rare earth oxides by means of emission spectra. I. Persistent lines in arc spectra of rare earth elements. *Analyst*, **74**, 95.

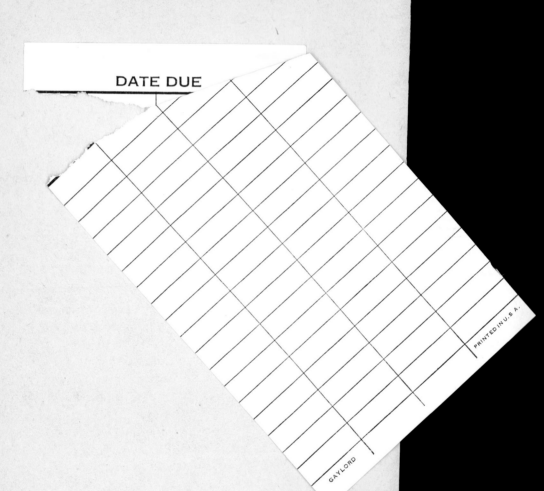

DATE DUE

GAYLORD   PRINTED IN U.S.A.